THE
GREENPEACE
🦋 LIVING
GUIDE

GREENPEACE

2008 Edition
www.greenpeace.ca

"What a handy book! Greenpeace has given us everyday tips to aid our environment. From the groceries we buy to the cleaning products we use, these are useful, practical ways to change how we relate to the environment around us."

—**Ed Broadbent**, former leader, federal New Democratic Party.

"*The Greenpeace Living Guide* provides a good summary of how every citizen must begin shifting priorities and changing habits. The changes described in this guide form the foundation of our commitment to improve quality of life for all people and particularly for future generations."

—**Rex Weyler**, former Greenpeace director, journalist and author of *Greenpeace: How a Group of Ecologists, Journalists, and Visionaries Changed the World*.

"A unique, down-to-earth, practical approach to organic and sustainable living. Don't just read it, make it happen!"

—**Arnold Taylor**, President of Canadian Organic Growers and organic farmer.

"Greenpeace is showing us all how we can take practical actions to protect the environment."

—**Marlo Raynolds**, PhD, Executive Director of the Pembina Institute.

"*The Greenpeace Living Guide* provides some great tips for improving your energy efficiency, promoting renewable electricity and reducing your environmental footprint."

—**Tom Heintzman**, President of Bullfrog Power Inc. and green energy advocate.

"We need to find new ways out of this dark age and *The Greenpeace Living Guide* is a tool to help you find your own right direction."

—**Michael Stadtländer**, world-renowned chef, organics advocate and owner of Eigensinn Farm.

"Use this Greenpeace guide, make better decisions and change some of your habits for the sake of our remarkable, natural world. It won't hurt a bit."

—**Sarah Harmer**, singer/songwriter and environmentalist.

"I hope that within my lifetime I see the day when reading a valuable green guide like this one is no longer necessary."

—**Margo Timmins**, lead singer, Cowboy Junkies.

"For decades I have been speaking about environmental issues and people often ask me what they can do in their daily life to help. *The Greenpeace Living Guide* provides a wealth of suggestions for them."

—**Robert Bateman**, artist and environmental advocate.

"Each person doing one thing at a time will create a momentum and movement that will make a difference. I wholly support Greenpeace and all their endeavours. Think and do something green."

—**Randy Bachman**, singer/songwriter and CBC Radio host.

"The planet's well-being is not just the purview of the wealthy or poor, known or lesser known individuals or solely the human race. The gift of this planet should be something we all strive toward protecting and enhancing. With this Living Guide, Greenpeace continues being a leading force in the implementation of the noble objective of individual responsibility and action."

—**Loreena McKennitt**, singer/songwriter.

THE
GREENPEACE
LIVING
GUIDE

Published by: Greenpeace Canada

Editorial oversight: Greenpeace Canada

Edited by: Amy Katz

Writing: Amy Katz

Art direction and design:
typotherapy+design inc.
www.typotherapy.com

Amy Katz is a writer and editor working on political,
urban and environmental issues.
amykatz@typotherapy.com

Printed in Canada by union labour on
100 percent post-consumer recycled, processed
chlorine-free paper using vegetable-based inks.

Second edition, May, 2008

ISBN 978-0-9732337-3-5

This book is dedicated to Greenpeace supporters in Canada and around the world.

To our new supporters, who have decided to share with us their help and their hope.

To our long-time supporters, who have stood by Greenpeace through so many tough battles and exhilarating victories.

To the supporters of the future, who will help to determine the direction and strength of the global environmental movement.

The vision and dedication of our supporters across the globe inspires all of us at Greenpeace every day. We want to take this opportunity to extend our deepest thanks.

If you are interested in becoming a Greenpeace supporter, please email us at: **living-guide@greenpeace.ca**

As with any venture, this book is imperfect, unfinished and in need of improvement. We encourage you to contact us at living-guide@greenpeace.ca with any comments or advice you might have. We also encourage you to read the caveats below.

1. Greenpeace does not endorse and cannot verify the accuracy of the content of the books, films and external websites listed in this book. In addition, we cannot endorse, recommend or guarantee any of the products listed by external sources.

2. This is not a health and safety guide. It is up to you to decide whether or not you can safely undertake any of the measures recommended here. In all cases—and especially when it comes to home renovations and improvements and safety and medical concerns—we recommend seeking expert advice. In addition, the products and practices listed here were chosen expressly to reduce negative human impacts on the environment. While some of the actions recommended might be good for your health, we did not write this guide with health in mind.

3. This publication is designed to give you some information you can use to make greener choices. It should be noted that neither the publisher nor the editor is engaged in providing medical, nutritional, safety, architectural, engineering or other professional services. In all cases, seek expert advice.

CONTENTS

The Greenpeace Living Guide colour system

Greenpeace living

Big Issues

Resources

Cleaning
Clothing and fabric
Electronics
Energy (at home)
Floor coverings
Food
Packaging
Paints, finishes and adhesives
Paper and printing
Plastics and non-stick coatings

Yard (and garden)
Wood
Water
Waste
Transportation
Toiletries
Tissue products
Special events
Shopping
Seafood

01

WELCOME TO THE GREENPEACE LIVING GUIDE

ABOUT GREENPEACE
ABOUT THIS BOOK
EDITOR'S INTRODUCTION
TOP TIPS

Thank you for choosing
The Greenpeace Living Guide.
We are honoured to be working side
by side with you to build a green
and peaceful future.

ABOUT
GREENPEACE

Greenpeace was founded in Vancouver in 1971 by a small group
of brave and dedicated activists. Today, Greenpeace is an international
environmental organization. We work on the issues we see as
fundamental to the health of our planet and its inhabitants: climate
change, ancient forests, oceans, sustainable agriculture, toxics and
nuclear disarmament.

Our environmental campaigns are characterized by our absolute
commitment to independent action. Greenpeace does not solicit funds
from governments or corporations. In fact, if we receive a large cheque
from a company, we return it. Our fierce independence allows us to take
on polluters without fear of financial reprisals. The only people we answer
to are our members, 2.8 million around the world.

A Greenpeace campaign is complex, strategic and anchored in scientific
research. We use peaceful direct action—dramatic acts of protest—to
draw international attention to urgent environmental issues. We engage
the public using websites, direct mail, publications, media, advertising,
meetings and one-on-one conversations. We work with the market,
convincing both institutional and individual customers to avoid
companies with destructive practices.

We undertake scientific research in our own lab at Exeter University in
the United Kingdom—we also work with independent scientists around
the world—and we use science to help shape our campaigns and expose
environmental issues. We propose innovative and original solutions like
'Greenfreeze,' Greenpeace's own low-impact refrigeration technology.

We lobby national governments—some of the best political campaigners
in the world work for Greenpeace. We also lobby international governments.
Greenpeace has consultative status to the United Nations. That means
we attend all major international environmental meetings and we make
sure our voice is heard. What are we saying? It's simple: protect our
planet for future generations. Before it's too late.

Greenpeace is effective. Over the thirty-six years we've been around, we've accomplished hundreds of concrete—and often international— victories for the environment. We propose detailed, realistic policies on clean energy, sustainable agriculture, toxic phase-outs and forest preservation on both the national and international scale. And we work to make sure they happen.

Greenpeace is brave. Our campaigners put themselves on the line for the environment. They wedge their bodies between whaling ships and whales on the high seas. They fearlessly expose corruption and destructive practices around the world. They confront politicians and CEOs, demanding answers. They work long hours, strategize constantly and share a genuine determination to implement real environmental solutions in Canada and around the world.

Greenpeace is effective. Greenpeace is brave. Greenpeace is also you. Our members are our shareholders, our investors, our partners and our source of power. Individuals like you around the world have banded together to form a safety net for the planet. The result: hope for the future. Greenpeace is one of the most effective environmental organizations in the world. Working with millions of individuals like you, we will find and implement solutions for our fragile planet. There is no other option.

For more information about Greenpeace Canada please call us toll-free at 1.800.320.7183 or visit us online at www.greenpeace.ca. For more information about Greenpeace International, please visit www.greenpeace.org

GREENPEACE'S
ENVIRONMENTAL CAMPAIGNS
ARE CHARACTERIZED BY OUR
ABSOLUTE COMMITMENT TO
INDEPENDENT ACTION.

ABOUT GREENPEACE

greenpeace
living

greenpeace

OUR FIERCE INDEPENDENCE ALLOWS US TO TAKE ON POLLUTERS WITHOUT FEAR OF FINANCIAL REPRISALS. THE ONLY PEOPLE WE ANSWER TO ARE OUR MEMBERS, 2.8 MILLION AROUND THE WORLD.

greenpeace
living

ABOUT THIS BOOK

The beginning. Starting can be the hardest part. The hardest part of putting together a book. The hardest part of changing your life. And the hardest part of changing the world.

Every day at Greenpeace, we come to work to chip away at environmental destruction. It can feel overwhelming, but we take it one step at a time. First, we look at the big picture. We identify the environmental issues that have a global reach, the ecosystems under serious threat, the situations we can change. Then we take one piece, one ecosystem, one region, one polluter at a time and we get on with it.

And that's where you come in. We are living in a society where, all too often, the consumer wins out over the citizen. So, while we work towards long-term political solutions to environmental destruction, we encourage you to use your 'consumer status' to help us demonstrate that change is possible.

Using this book will have tangible results. First, you will be supporting the kind of production you want to see—just, organic, non-toxic. Second, by refusing to buy products that contribute unnecessarily to environmental destruction, you will be sending polluters a strong message: produce responsibly or you will lose your market.

In addition, you will be reducing your own, personal impact on the planet. You will use less water and less energy, produce less garbage, leak fewer toxins into the environment and destroy fewer acres of ancient forest. And, as a bonus, you will be getting exercise, eating well and taking fewer chemicals into your body.

Finally, you will be helping us call into question fundamental ideas about economic progress. Built into our economic system is the tenet of constant growth—a 'healthy' economy is tied to ever-increasing consumption. This leads to the commodification of, well, everything—food, water, forests, plants, ideas. It also leads to the endless exploitation of people and of resources.

The ingredients for life—what some people call the global commons—belong to every human being. The broader goal of the environmental movement must be to secure equitable and sustainable access to the commons for everyone. Thank you for starting with this book. And thank you from all of us at Greenpeace for helping us change the world.

How to use this book. *The Greenpeace Living Guide* is designed to go with you to the grocery store, the hardware store, to work and back home again. From choosing cleaning products to deciding what to have for dinner, this guide offers real solutions for environmental living.

The guide is organized alphabetically, like an encyclopedia. If you are looking for apples at the grocery store, you can look up 'food' and you will find quick hits of information that will help you decide what to buy. For more detail, consult the 'big issues' section where you will find short essays on environmental issues like ancient forest destruction and climate change.

You will also find a list of resources—from government climate change websites to ancient forest friendly paper databases—to help you go even deeper into environmental issues. The sources used to research and compile this book are listed by section at the back.

This guide will help you be an environmental consumer. It will also help you be an environmental citizen. Greenpeace knows that to make change, you have to make waves. Throughout this guide you will find opportunities to take action. From writing politicians to asking your local grocery store to stock ancient forest friendly products, taking political action is the most important thing you can do to help protect the environment.

This book is a work in progress. Future editions will reflect evolving environmental issues, new technologies, political developments and, most importantly, your input. Please write us at living-guide@greenpeace.ca with your feedback. Tell us how the guide worked for you and what you'd like to see included in the next edition. This guide—like all of Greenpeace's work to protect the environment—is a collaborative effort.

EDITOR'S INTRODUCTION

The magazines, the cable channels and the self-help books tell us that there's hope for each one of us, as long as we're willing to change our lifestyles. You can find love—just be positive, don't return his phone calls and use eye cream. You can be healthy—just eat right, lose weight and drink lots of water. And you can save the environment—just buy hemp, eat organic and ride your bike. To engage life, change your lifestyle. The problem starts with you, the answer ends with you. Unfortunately, unless you're going through life sealed in a Ziploc bag, it's not that simple. We can change our lifestyles, but we're not making our changes in a vacuum. The state of the world is going to intervene.

Take the example of genetically engineered (GE) foods. As you probably know, genetic engineering is different from traditional plant breeding in that it allows corporations to breed the unbreedable—say, corn and viruses or tomatoes and fish. I'm not going to argue that the universe produced the rutabaga from some divine template that should remain inviolate forever. The universe produced a lot of things, we've switched the furniture around since then, and it's reasonable to use science to trump nature when nature comes in the form of locusts or the plague.

The problem with GE food is that corporations and scientists honestly don't know what it will do to your health or to traditional and organic crops. There have been no long-term health studies on the effects of consuming GE food. There have been no long-term tests on the effects GE crops might have on biodiversity (the variety of plants and animals on the planet) or on the health of our food supply. In the meantime, GE pollen is blowing all over the place, crossbreeding with traditional plants and showing up as weeds in traditional fields. And, by the way, you are already eating GE food and have been for more than ten years.

There is only one reason why GE food is out in the world, reproducing itself, at best prematurely and at worst as a threat to your health and to the environment: because it is profitable for corporations. Large biotechnology companies like Monsanto and Bayer sell their patented seeds to farmers. The crops are generally engineered to resist a specific patented pesticide or herbicide. In Canada, Monsanto's Roundup Ready canola, for example, has been engineered to resist repeated sprayings with Monsanto's patented Roundup herbicide.

GE food was not created as a result of consumer demand. GE food was created to profit corporations. And the Canadian government has stepped out of the way, a decision that makes Canada one of a handful of global exceptions. The entire European Union labels GE food, and countries from Brazil to Japan have imposed moratoriums on GE crops. In Canada (and in the United States) there are almost no rules. No labels for products containing genetically engineered ingredients, no long-term health testing required for new genetically engineered organisms, no penalties for Monsanto when its GE crops blow into traditional fields. Canada won't even ratify the Biosafety Protocol, the only international agreement regulating the trade of GE food.

So how does lifestyle factor into the reasonable attempts by scientists, farmers, citizens and non-governmental organizations to demand government research and regulation for GE food? Well, it does and it doesn't. You can buy your organic rainforest crunch, but it is entirely possible that, one day soon, no-one will be able to guarantee that it doesn't contain genetically engineered ingredients. The same is true, writ large, for climate change. Get rid of your car, but it won't stop the polar ice caps from melting. Stop using pesticides on your lawn, but you will probably still end up with lead in your bones and PCBs in your blood.

That doesn't mean that your lifestyle won't make a difference. Change is facilitated when pressure comes from all directions. If you buy organic, producers and retailers will notice, and they will respond. Farm workers and consumers will be exposed to fewer toxins and fewer pesticides will be dumped into the ground. There are very good reasons to make solid personal choices for the environment.

The problem is not the issue of personal choice—it's the doctrine of personal choice. We are constantly being told that change begins with us, that only we can solve our own problems, that we are the authors of our destinies. I believe that these are, in fact, ideological statements, rooted in a free market aversion to collective action. To get ourselves through to the next century, we will need to shake off the phantasm of an exclusively personal destiny and couple our individual choices with real, penalty-laden national and international environmental regulations. To get ourselves through to the next century, we will need a collective privileging of human lives and futures over corporate profits.

In other words, we need to make political change, something we can't do as individuals. And something we can't do without challenging, in a serious and uncomfortable way, the existing order. So, yes, let's change our lifestyles and reduce our personal impacts on the environment. It will help to nudge us closer to the world we want. But, at some point (and I would argue that that point would be now), to prevent global environmental breakdown, we are going to have to embark on a course of action that questions some of the fundamental tenets of our economic system.

The logic of the market is destroying the planet. We will not save the planet by turning the free market on itself and buying hybrid cars. We will save the planet by forcing our governments to mandate real environmental regulations. We will save the planet by refusing to allow the requirements of the market to dictate our health, our preferences, our sense of reality and the course of our lives. In the meantime, buy organic.

Amy Katz
Editor, *The Greenpeace Living Guide*

greenpeace
living

greenpeace

Here are *The Greenpeace Living Guide*'s top ten tips for reducing your personal ecological footprint. Please remember—no-one can tell you exactly what to do to make the world a better place. We can't say definitively that airplane travel is worse for the planet than, say, an over-packaged, meat-heavy junk food diet. The aim of this section—and of this guide in general—is to supply you with some information. This guide is one of Greenpeace's contributions to the global conversation about the environment—a conversation we want to continue with you.

To tell us what you think, please contact us at living-guide@greenpeace.ca

GREENPEACE GUIDE
TOP TIPS˙

1. Drive less (or better yet, don't drive). The Union of Concerned Scientists ranked a range of consumer activities in terms of environmental impact. The number one culprit: cars and light trucks. [1] Walk, bike or get a monthly pass for your local public transportation system. If you have to drive, carpool or car share whenever possible. Choose a car with the best mileage per litre that you can find.

2. Eat fewer animal products (or don't eat them at all). Meat and dairy products are incredibly resource-intensive. First of all, they waste other sources of food. The Worldwatch Institute estimates that the total amount of soy and grain fed to livestock in the US each year could feed everyone on the planet five times over. [2]

Animal production also wastes massive amounts of land, energy and water. Researchers at the University of Chicago estimate that if an average, meat-eating American switched to a plant-based diet, they would save approximately 1.5 tonnes of greenhouse gas emissions each year. [3] (To give you an idea of scale, recent statistics put Canadian per capita greenhouse gas emissions at about 23 tonnes per year.) [4] Meat and other animal products also require more land to produce than vegetables, fruits and grains.

3. Eat organic, locally grown, GE-free food. Organic food is grown without synthetic chemicals. It's also produced without genetically engineered (GE) organisms. And, when you buy local produce, you cut out the greenhouse gas emissions required to transport food around the world. Unfortunately, GE food is not currently labelled in Canada. When buying non-organic, processed foods, avoid products containing corn, soy, canola or cottonseed oil. These ingredients are likely to be genetically engineered.

4. Buy less. When making a purchase, ask yourself a standard set of questions. What is it made out of? How was it made? Under what conditions? How far did it travel to get to you? Who's really profiting from your purchase? Does it contain ancient forest wood or hazardous chemicals? Can you reuse it? Will it last? Can it be fixed when it breaks? Can it be recycled? Or, better yet, can you reduce your overall consumption and skip it completely?

5. Choose fair trade. Our global economic system uses whatever it can—the environment, human beings—to generate profit. In addition, rich countries have rigged international trade in their own favour. Countries like the US subsidize domestic industries while demanding 'barrier-free' trade from the rest of the world. Our current trading system is having a devastating impact on the lives of human beings and on the health of the planet.

Look for products that are fair trade certified. Demand that your local stores carry fair trade certified products. Find out more about the world trading system and how you can help change it.

6. Reduce airplane travel. It's surprising but true: eliminating or reducing airplane travel may be one of the most important things you can do for the environment. Avoid planes for short trips—take the train or the bus. Plan local vacations and use video and teleconferencing instead of flying to meetings. You can also use carbon offset programs that allow you to plant trees or invest in green energy to help compensate for climate-damaging flights. (Please note, not all carbon offset programs are created equal—make sure to do some research first.) The best thing to do: fly less.

7. Reduce waste (including energy waste). Buy in bulk and bring your own bags and containers to the store. Use a reusable, stainless steel mug for take-out drinks. Set aside time to explore your municipality's website or literature to find out what do to with hazardous waste—including used electronics—and exactly what materials are accepted in your municipal recycling program. Use compact fluorescent light bulbs, turn off lights when you leave the room, turn down the thermostat at night and retrofit your home for energy efficiency.

8. Look to your municipality. Municipalities across Canada are incredible sources of information about the environment and daily life. Go to your municipality's website or call with any questions you have about how to reduce the environmental impacts of your household or workplace. Start by asking them about recycling, hazardous waste, water use reduction, pesticide-free lawn care and rebates and incentives for low-flow toilets and other efficient products.

9. Tell everyone. Word of mouth is the best advertising. Tell friends and family what you are doing. Forward emails with green tips to your personal email lists and share this book with everyone you know. Start conversations, blogs, email lists and green committees in your neighbourhood and at work. The goal: to make green living the norm. Show them how it's done.

10. Get (even more) political. One of the most important things you can do for the environment is to work for systemic change. Canada needs environmental and labour regulations with teeth and politicians with the guts and the mandate to enforce the law. Internationally, we need a regulatory system that can keep pace with the ever-expanding system of global trade. And, most importantly, in Canada and around the world, we need economic systems that privilege people and the planet over profit.

See 'EVERYDAY ACTIVIST TIPS' for some ideas on how to get political in your daily life.

Right: Choosing organic food is one of the top ten things you can do for the environment.

Bucking the trend of our consumer society isn't a simple thing to do. But it isn't impossible either. Here are a few suggestions for creating long-lasting habits and making green living a seamless part of your everyday life.

* **A recycling system.** Take a day or two to find out what your municipality recycles and what they don't. Find out where to take your hazardous waste, including cleaning products, compact fluorescent light bulbs, batteries and motor oil.

  Old electronics are usually classified as hazardous waste, too, but you might want to do a bit of research about what to do with them when you're done. Are there not-for-profits or schools in your area looking for used ink cartridges or computers? Can you take your cell phone or computer back to the manufacturer?

  Once you've figured it all out, post a recycling schedule, a list of recyclables and a few key phone numbers on the fridge. It will only get easier from there.

* **A shopping/take-out system.** Spend a few hours putting together a shopping/take-out kit. Assemble some cloth bags and clean containers for shopping. Source a reusable coffee mug and some food-safe, reusable take-out containers. Include a cloth napkin, reusable cutlery and chopsticks and a thermos.

  Make it easy to use and keep it all clean and ready to go. Right there, you've already cut out piles of take-out containers, disposable coffee cups, plastic tubs and plastic bags.

✳ **A book of lists.** There are a few key lists you need to carry with you, in your head or in your wallet, every time you go shopping. Some of these lists we can provide for you; other ones you will have to develop for yourself as you go along. Some list examples include unsustainable seafood, foods containing genetically engineered ingredients and plastics to avoid.

You can also keep lists of good items like ancient forest friendly tissue products and electronics manufacturers with good toxics and take-back policies. Eventually, you will be able to shop green without even thinking about it. Until then, get yourself a little notebook and record your green finds and epiphanies.

✳ **An email or phone call a week.** Engaging government, industry and your community is a big part of living green. Commit to at least one email or phone call each week. If you discover that your local grocery store doesn't offer post-consumer recycled toilet paper, for example, call head office and let them know you want to see it on the shelves the next time you come in. If you are angry that our federal government refuses to take real action on climate change, take a moment and send the Environment Minister an email.

An easy way to help meet your enviro action quota is to visit Greenpeace's website at www.greenpeace.ca and sign up as a cyber-activist. The action points will land in your inbox each month.

Part 02

02

GREENPEACE LIVING

CLEANING
CLOTHING AND FABRIC
ELECTRONICS
ENERGY (AT HOME)
FLOOR COVERINGS
FOOD
PACKAGING
PAINTS, FINISHES AND ADHESIVES
PAPER AND PRINTING
PLASTICS AND NON-STICK COATINGS
SEAFOOD
SHOPPING
SPECIAL EVENTS
TISSUE PRODUCTS
TOILETRIES
TRANSPORTATION
WASTE
WATER
WOOD
YARD (AND GARDEN)

Think of it as a treasure hunt. It's going to be fun, you'll need a sense of adventure and creative thinking will help. When it comes to living green, there are a lot of personal decisions that come into play. You're going to have to balance the different environmental concerns attached to each product you buy. It's not always an easy call, but we'll give you some of the information you need to help you make the best choices for the environment. **Each section** is broken into two parts. 'Where to start' gives you a list of simple, point form ideas. 'Want more?' goes into more depth, providing details and web resources. Along the way you'll find 'green business tips,' 'green student tips' and reading suggestions. Some of the information in this guide might be difficult to hear—the news, more often than not, isn't great. But don't be discouraged—it's better to do one thing than nothing at all. And along with the hard facts, you'll find real solutions that will make a difference to your own, personal environmental impacts.

Please note that sources are listed by section at the back of this book.

CLEANING

OVERVIEW

Cleaning products—which can contain synthetic scents, petrochemicals and other harmful substances—can be big contributors to poor indoor air quality. In addition to generating toxic emissions, cleaning practices can use excessive amounts of water, energy and packaging.

Cleaning, however, is a good news category. You can have a fresh-scrubbed home and do the right thing for the environment at the same time. It's not hard to significantly reduce your household use of toxic chemicals in just a few days. Give yourself a week to explore some products and create new rituals. And keep track of how much you used to spend on cleaning products. You're going to save money here, too.

Fact:

According to studies conducted by the US Environmental Protection Agency, indoor levels of common organic pollutants in US homes can be two to five times higher than outdoor levels. Why? In part due to common household products like cleansers, disinfectants, cosmetics, paints and varnishes. [1]

Where to start:

✳ Avoid products containing harsh chemicals and synthetic scents.

✳ Try baking soda and white vinegar to clean (they work!).

✳ Avoid over-packaged products. Choose nature-friendly cleaning products in bulk and in concentrated form.

✳ Choose washable, reusable towels or cloths over disposable tissue products like paper towels.

✳ Avoid dry cleaning. If you are going to dry clean, find a provider who doesn't use perchloroethylene (PERC) or other toxic solvents.

✳ Wash clothes in cold water whenever possible and hang to dry.

✳ If you are going to use toxic substances, make sure you dispose of them separately from normal household garbage since these products should not be landfilled. Call your municipality's toxic trash phone line or recycling hotline for more information.

Want more?

1. Choose products that are free of harsh chemicals and synthetic fragrances.

Like so many products on the market (dyes, fabrics, fertilizers, plastics), many household cleaning products contain chemicals derived from petroleum which are inherently hazardous in their chemical makeup. Many solvents (used to help dissolve or suspend dirt and grease) and surfactants (which lower the surface tension of water so detergents interact better with oil and grease) are suspected or known to be harmful to health and the environment. Other chemicals can emit volatile organic compounds (VOCs) during use, polluting indoor air quality and affecting human health. There are other reasons to avoid petrochemicals in cleaning products. They are derived from a non-renewable resource and can have serious environmental impacts during their extraction, manufacture, use and disposal. At a minimum, look for products that are biodegradable within a specific time frame and free of synthetic fragrances and other harsh chemicals. If you are going to use products containing hazardous chemicals, use them sparingly. When you're done, do not put them down the drain or out for regular garbage pick-up. Contact your municipality and find out your options for dealing safely with hazardous waste. Make sure to keep all cleaning products—even 'non-toxic' ones—out of children's reach.

2. Read labels and decode claims.

So, you want to avoid harsh chemicals in products, but how do you do it? A first step is to avoid products that come with warning signs like 'poison' or 'danger' or 'corrosive.' It's a good bet that they contain toxic chemicals or, at the very least, present a direct exposure risk to you.

To date, there are few reliable eco-labels when it comes to cleaning products. Some claims do, however, carry more weight than others. Terms like 'non-toxic,' 'natural' and 'fragrance-free' aren't regulated and can be meaningless. Even the term 'organic' is suspect unless it's referring to specific certified organic, plant-based ingredients.

Look for concrete terms like 'phosphate-free,' 'no solvents' and 'plant-based' (as opposed to petroleum-based) but keep in mind that these claims should have a credible third party certification label attached.

If a product claims to be biodegradable, make sure the manufacturer lists how long it takes to biodegrade or look for 'without effluent treatment processes' which usually means the product should biodegrade when used with a septic system or poured directly onto land or into water. [2]

For help choosing products free of some hazardous chemicals, visit the federal government's 'Environmental Choice' website at: www.environmentalchoice.com

For more information on eco-labels, visit the Consumer's

Union site on labelling at:
www.eco-labels.org

For detailed information about toxic chemicals in cleaning products from the Labour Alliance Environmental Society, visit: www.leas.ca

3. Try using vinegar and baking soda.

If you want to try making your own cleansers, look inside your kitchen cupboard. White vinegar and baking soda are hero ingredients.

White vinegar (5 percent acetic acid) is a mild disinfectant and can be used to clean glass, remove calcium deposits and cut grease. When cleaning glass, dilute with four parts water.

Baking soda is a magical substance. It can be used as a mild abrasive to clean bathtubs and sinks. Just apply it to a damp sponge, scrub and rinse. It also removes stains, deodorizes and softens fabrics.

4. Choose products that are available in bulk and concentrated form.

Many health food stores and co-ops sell less toxic cleaning products in bulk form. Bring in your own, reusable containers to save on packaging. Products like laundry detergent that come in concentrated form help to cut down on packaging and transportation costs at the same time. If you are buying pre-packaged products, look for bottles and boxes made from post-consumer recycled materials and make sure they are recyclable in your area.

5. Wash responsibly.

Laundry offers a prime opportunity to save water and energy and cut down on your own personal toxic load. Look for biodegradable, unscented, un-dyed, phosphate-free, natural laundry soaps and avoid bleach. If you can, use water- and energy-efficient washers and dryers. Avoid the dryer whenever possible—hang your clothes to dry. Use the cold water cycle as often as you can—your clothes will last longer.

Avoid dry cleaning—many clothes that say 'dry clean only' can be hand washed in cold water. If you prefer to dry clean, find a dry cleaner who doesn't use perchloroethylene (PERC), a toxic solvent used by most dry cleaners. Some dry cleaners use petroleum hydrocarbon instead of PERC as an 'environmentally friendly' solvent. Petroleum hydrocarbon (oil again!) comes from a non-renewable resource and has been linked to concerns about toxicity and ground-water contamination. Look for a dry cleaner who uses carbon dioxide or wet cleaning. [3]

For more information on energy-efficient appliances from the federal government, visit: www.oee.nrcan.gc.ca

For a listing of 'green' dry cleaners from the Canadian Centre for Pollution Prevention, visit: www.c2p2online.com. Definitions of 'green' dry cleaning may vary—call dry cleaners to confirm their methods and practices.

Right: Laundry is a great opportunity to reduce toxics, water and energy use.

CLOTHING AND FABRIC

OVERVIEW

Like most consumer items, clothing is the result of a long and populated chain of production. Serious environmental, social and labour concerns are associated with every aspect of an average t-shirt's journey from cottonseed to closet. The ideal wardrobe is made without the use of toxic

chemicals from organic, fair trade certified fabrics, assembled and retailed by a worker's co-op or union workplace and sold to you without the use of gender, class or cultural stereotypes. We're also tempted to write that it doesn't exist. But, as with most products, a little commitment and compromise will find you something close to what you're looking for.

Organic, fair trade certified cotton is increasingly available (it should be noted, though, that the fair trade certification applies only to the cotton itself—not to the working conditions under which the garment is assembled). Clothing made under fair labour conditions is out there too but you will have to dig to find it. As for the images of young, thin strangers smiling at you from billboards, demanding that you acquire everything, every season, all the time—we can't help you there. It's up to you to decide that you do (if you do) finally have everything you need. And that's the most environmental decision of all.

Fact:

In 2003/2004, genetically engineered cotton accounted for 34 percent of the international cotton trade. [1]

Must read:

For information on labour rights and working conditions in the garment industry, visit: www.cleanclothes.org and www.maquilasolidarity.org

Where to start:

* Buy vintage clothing and exchange favourite items with friends.

* Learn to patch, knit, crochet, sew patterns and invent your own creations.

* Choose clothing made out of recycled fabrics.

* Choose organic, fair trade cotton.

* Choose clothing made in worker-run co-ops or union workplaces. For more information, visit: www.sweatfree.org/shopping

* Choose clothing made with natural, sustainable fibres like bamboo and hemp.

* Avoid clothing and fabric with chemical stain-proofing and permanent-press treatments.

* Ask retailers and manufacturers about their policies on toxic chemicals, sustainable fabrics and labour conditions.

* To participate in anti-sweatshop campaigns, visit: www.maquilasolidarity.org, www.cleanclothes.org and www.behindthelabel.org

Simple step:

When you get home after a shopping trip, take a minute to visit the retailer's website and send them a quick email—many of them have comment boxes right on the homepage. Ask them about their policies on toxic chemicals, sustainable fabrics and labour conditions.

CLOTHING AND FABRIC

Want more?

1. Buy fewer clothes.

One of the best ways to reduce your impact on the environment is to reduce consumption. Choose clothes that are made to last. Learn to patch, knit, crochet, sew and generally troubleshoot. Develop relationships with tailors and shoe repair folks—have a plan in place before your favourite boot springs a hole in its sole. Once you make clothing rehabilitation a part of your life, it will become a habit like any other.

2. Choose pre-loved clothing.

The possibilities for populating your wardrobe with used clothing are endless. You can pick up vintage items at boutiques, consignment shops, garage sales or online. You can organize a clothing exchange with friends and pick through their closets in exchange for your own lovely cast-offs. Shopping used requires some creativity and a sense of your own style but it's worth it. You'll save money and you'll spare the environment a whack of pesticides, waste, water, packaging and greenhouse gas emissions.

3. Pass your own clothes on to others.

Congratulations—you're now sourcing your wardrobe from friends, vintage shops, garage sales and websites. You've taken your old shoes to a local shoe repair and you've managed to patch up your favourite sweater on your own.

Now it's time to go through your wardrobe and get rid of every single thing you don't wear and, face it, will never wear. Be merciless. Other people will make good use of any clean, intact items languishing in your closet.

Once you're done, you have a lot of options. The best one: contact a local shelter or drop-in program and find out if they accept donations of well-maintained used clothing. Other options: have a garage sale, sell items online, give used children's clothing to friends or organize a clothing exchange.

Whatever you do, recycle it all into loving hands.

4. Choose organic, fair trade cotton over conventional cotton.

Cotton accounts for approximately 39 percent of the world's fibre needs. [2] Here, issues begin at the molecular level, where corporations have genetically engineered strains of cotton that produce their own pesticides or resist patented herbicides. In 2003/2004, genetically engineered (GE) cotton accounted for approximately 21 percent of cotton acreage around the world and 77 percent in the US. [3] GE cotton has found its way into feed (for animals), food (for people) and clothing.

Once in the ground, cotton—both conventional and organic—is one of the most heavily-irrigated crops in the world. Non-organic cotton is also one of the most pesticide-intensive crops on the planet. According to a recent report by the Environmental Justice Foundation

in collaboration with the Pesticide Action Network UK, cotton accounts for close to 16 percent of world insecticide releases—more than any other individual crop. [4]

Workers exposed to pesticides can suffer health impacts including damage to the nervous system, damage to the endocrine system, various types of cancers and skin and eye irritation. [5] Pesticides can also have devastating effects on the environment, poisoning wildlife and leeching into water sources. [6]

When cotton is ready for market, its sale can be governed by global trade rules that prevent countries from subsidizing domestic agriculture. Some countries, however, choose to ignore the rules. According to Oxfam, in 2001/2002, the US government subsidized its cotton industry to the tune of $3.9 billion. Recently, these practices have forced global prices to the lowest they've been since the Great Depression in the 1930s. The result for cotton farmers in Central and West Africa over that same period: losses of $301 million—the equivalent of close to one-quarter of what the region received in American aid. 7

Luckily, organic cotton clothing is now widely available at specialty boutiques, health food stores and even at some major retailers. In addition, fair trade certified cotton is available from specific retailers in Canada and around the world. Please note that fair trade certified cotton only covers the agricultural stage of production. It does not necessarily guarantee 'sweat free' or ethical conditions at the manufacturing stage.

For information about where to find fair trade certified cotton, visit: www.transfair.ca (search for cotton products).

For information on where to find organic cotton clothing, visit: www.organicexchange.org

5. Choose clothing made under just working conditions.

According to Sweatshop Watch, a sweatshop is a workplace that violates the law; fails to provide workers with a living wage; imposes long hours and poor working conditions; subjects workers to arbitrary discipline including harassment or verbal abuse and/or uses intimidation when workers attempt to complain or organize a union. 8

While global trade regimes use penalties and tariffs to force (some) countries to abide by trade agreements, international labour standards (and environmental agreements, for that matter) have no real enforcement mechanisms. In addition, corporations are rarely held accountable by governments, consumers or industry organizations for poor labour or environmental practices.

Workers, anti-sweatshop activists and fair trade movements are all making concerted attempts to address the working conditions across the chain of production. Many activists are also aware of consumer demand for ethical shopping guides. Unfortunately, there are no simple answers and, currently, no comprehensive 'ethical clothing' certification system exists. In addition, some activists believe that it's important for consumers to do more than just purchase from a list. Sustained citizen engagement is an integral part of the work to change the way global trade works. We need to ask questions, we need to be curious and we need to hold retailers and manufacturers to account.

Here are a few questions you can ask next time you go clothing shopping. Make them your own and bring them with you each time you shop. You might meet with some blank looks, you might have to talk to a manager, you might end up speaking to head office, but it's worth it. Be polite, but firm. You might also choose to fill out a customer comment card or simply go to the retailer's website and send them a quick email. Whomever you speak to, however you do it, asking questions is an excellent way to begin sourcing your own ethical wardrobe:

- Does your company produce clothing under just working conditions?
- Do you have a list of factories where your clothes are made? Does it include wages and working conditions?
- Do you have a code of conduct protecting human rights and forbidding child labour and unsafe working conditions in the factories that make your clothes?
- Is there an independent monitoring agency that makes sure your contractors and sub-contractors live up to the code?
- What do you do when you discover violations of the code?

Although, as mentioned, no comprehensive certification system exists for clothing, Sweat Free Communities has compiled a 'Shop with a conscience' guide of garments produced under fair labour conditions: www.sweatfree.org/shopping

The union Unite Here also offers information on union-made clothing: www.unitehere.org/buyunion

6. Avoid synthetic fabrics derived from petrochemicals.

As usual, oil is the culprit, this time in the form of synthetic fabrics like polyester and nylon derived from petrochemicals. These fabrics come from a non-renewable resource and, according to the Union of Concerned Scientists, generate hazardous waste during production and don't biodegrade. [9]

Watch out, too, for oil's agricultural cousin—corporate-controlled, genetically engineered (GE) corn—which seems to be waiting in the wings to take over where petroleum will, inevitably, have to leave off. Right now, GE corn is being touted as a miracle replacement for petroleum-based products from plastics to fabrics. A fashion show at a recent

biotechnology conference in Toronto featured corn-based creations from designers including Oscar de la Renta and Halston. Unfortunately, Canada has no mandatory labelling laws in place for GE fabrics or food.

For more information about Greenpeace's campaign to label GE ingredients, visit: www.greenpeace.ca

7. Choose sustainable fabrics.

Choose natural fabrics made from renewable resources like hemp, wool, linen and bamboo. Bamboo, in particular, is a good option—it's fast growing and can thrive without pesticides, fertilizers or irrigation. But, as with any eco-trend, there are caveats. You're looking for sustainable bamboo that wasn't grown at the expense of natural forests. You also want to know how the fabric was treated—some processes are more chemical-intensive than others. [10] Hemp is another star fabric. It can be grown without the use of synthetic pesticides, herbicides or fungicides and thrives in Canada's cool climate.

8. Avoid chemical treatments.

Many fabrics are treated with chemicals to resist wrinkling, staining or moths. These often contain perfluorochemicals—the chemicals found in non-stick treatments on cookware—and other harmful substances like formaldehyde. (See safety note.)

9. Avoid chemical dyes.

Here, once again, oil rears its ugly head in the form of petrochemical dyes that can pollute waterways. When you have the option, look for un-dyed or botanically-dyed clothes (but be careful—these can fade or bleed in the wash).

Green business tips:

A) Implement a 'no sweat' policy in your workplace, school or city. The Maquila Solidarity Network offers a series of suggestions about how to make sure bulk clothing purchases like uniforms and t-shirts are manufactured under acceptable working conditions. For more information, visit: www.maquilasolidarity.org/nosweat

B) Ask your company to integrate Green Chemistry protocols into their supplier requirements. To consult with a green chemistry expert, visit the Canadian Green Chemistry Network at www.greenchemistry.ca

Green student tip:

Students across North America are mobilizing to make sure all school-related apparel is manufactured under fair conditions. Bring the sweat-free schools campaign to your college or university or participate in an existing chapter. For more information, visit: www.studentsagainstsweatshops.org

Safety note:

Chemical treatments, while often very toxic, can be used to make items flame retardant. The Union of Concerned Scientists cautions: "Consider carefully before abandoning this safety feature, especially with children's sleepwear." Balance this with the fact that many flame retardants— and brominated flame retardants in particular—can contaminate indoor air quality and affect human health.

ELECTRONICS

OVERVIEW

Most electronic products—your computer, your CD player, your television set—contain hazardous substances like brominated flame retardants (BFR), heavy metals and polyvinyl chloride (PVC). These substances—particularly BFRs—contaminate indoor air quality and can affect human health. The more toxics-laden consumer products you have in your home, the more contaminated the air.

Hazardous substances also make products difficult or impossible to recycle safely. Right now, a percentage of electronic waste is routinely exported by rich countries, often in violation of international law. In the US, it is estimated that 50 to 80 percent of e-waste collected for recycling is destined for export. 1 In many countries, recycling is often done by hand, in scrap yards, exposing workers to hazardous substances including lead, PVC, brominated flame retardants and mercury.

Fact:

Electronic waste now makes up 5 percent of all municipal solid waste worldwide and is the fastest growing component of the municipal solid waste stream. 2 According to Environment Canada, approximately 140,000 tonnes of e-waste end up in Canadian landfills every year. 3

Must read:

Greenpeace Guide to Greener Electronics. www.greenpeace.org/greenerelectronics

Where to start:

* Don't buy gadgets you don't need. Corporations make enormous efforts to sell us ever-morphing gadgets and ever-larger televisions. Whenever possible, opt out.

* Choose electronics brands that have made commitments to the phase-out of hazardous substances— specifically, polyvinyl chloride (PVC) and brominated flame retardants (BFRs).

* Contact your municipality and/or the manufacturer for recycling options and look into donating gently used products to schools and not-for-profits.

* Electronics are considered hazardous waste. Find out from your municipality how to dispose of them.

Want more?

1. Choose a manufacturer with clear and responsible chemical and recycling policies.

Some companies are working to phase out toxic substances and create effective recycling programs. Other companies refuse to implement green policies. In 2006, Greenpeace began ranking the world's electronics companies on their chemical and recycling policies. Greenpeace is asking companies to:

* **Substitute harmful chemicals in the production of electronics.** This will prevent both the exposure of workers to these hazardous substances and the contamination of communities close to production facilities. Greenpeace is particularly concerned about brominated flame retardants (BFRs) and polyvinyl chloride (PVC). Both substances generate highly toxic chemicals called dioxins when burned. In addition, their manufacturing processes involve the use of extremely hazardous materials.

Alternatives to both BFRs and PVC exist and many companies have now committed to phasing in safer materials.

* **Implement effective recycling programs.** Greenpeace is asking companies to take back electronic waste even in countries in which this is not required by law.

Other elements of an effective recycling program include supplying customers with information on what do to with their old electronics and offering reports on the amount of electronic waste collected and recycled. Greenpeace is also asking companies to support Individual Producer

Responsibility (IPR)—the idea that each company should take care of its own electronic waste.

For links to information about the recycling programs of major electronics manufacturers, visit: www.epsc.ca/r_links.html

2. Recycle or donate used electronics.

If you are thinking about buying a new electronics item, contact the manufacturer and make sure they provide a comprehensive take-back program. If they don't, and you still want to buy their product, contact your municipality to find out if they have an electronics recycling program.

Some municipalities provide depots for dropping off used computers, printers, scanners and other electronics.

Some not-for-profits and government programs will accept gently used computers as donations. Some programs even accept ink cartridges, software and computer accessories. Many places will also re-fill empty ink cartridges for you.

These, however, are all stop gap measures. The real answer: Individual Producer Responsibility regulations at all levels of government.

3. Ask before buying.

As a customer or potential customer, you have some leverage. Before buying phones, audio equipment, televisions or computers, contact the manufacturer and find out what their policies are on hazardous substances like PVC and brominated flame retardants. Ask the manufacturer of your computer or television if they support legislation enforcing Individual Producer Responsibility in Canada.

4. Turn it off. Save on stand-by.

When you're not using a television, computer or stereo, turn it off. You can also plug electronics into a power bar (just make sure the outlet can handle it). After you turn everything off, you can switch off the power bar too to save on stand-by electricity use.

ELECTRONICS

5. Choose energy-efficient electronics.

For some of the most energy-efficient products on the market, look for the ENERGY STAR logo.

Choose electronics and equipment including computers, monitors and printers with an ENERGY STAR rating.

For a list of ENERGY STAR-rated products, visit: www.oee.nrcan.gc.ca

You an also reduce the energy impact of your electronics by using a solar-powered charger for portable music players, laptops, cellphones and other related gadgets.

For more information on solar-powered chargers, visit: www.treehugger.com

6. Choose a laptop over a desktop.

If it's practical for you, choose a laptop instead of a desktop—according to Greenpeace International, they consume five times less energy. 4

Green business tips:

A) ENERGY STAR offers a full range of certified energy-efficient office equipment including photocopiers, printers, computers and fax machines. Visit: www.oee.nrcan.gc.ca

For more information from the Silicon Valley Toxics Coalition on green certifications for computers, visit: http://svtc.igc.org

B) Visit Industry Canada's 'Computers for Schools' website to find out how to recycle your surplus IT equipment to schools, public libraries and not-for-profits. Visit: www.cfsope.ic.gc.ca

C) If your workplace doesn't currently recycle electronics, try creating an in-house program. Contact your municipality for advice.

Right: E-waste makes up 5 percent of municipal solid waste worldwide and is the fastest growing component of the municipal solid waste stream.

ENERGY (AT HOME)

OVERVIEW

Canadian consumers use energy directly: to move our cars, to heat and cool our homes, to power electric appliances. Canadian consumers use energy indirectly: to cut down forests for our toilet paper, to move an avocado thousands of miles from food to table, to power the factories that churn out BlackBerrys and blue jeans. From industry to agriculture, from transportation to energy extraction itself, our need for energy continues to grow.

Energy use contributes heavily to the most serious environmental problem on the planet today: climate change. Greenhouse gases—in particular carbon dioxide—are released when we burn fossil fuels. Greenhouse gases build up in the atmosphere and lead to global warming. Today, after close to two hundred years of intense fossil fuel use by a relatively small group of countries, the average global temperature is rising. According to a recent assessment by the United Nations Intergovernmental Panel on Climate Change, eleven of the last twelve years (1995-2006) rank among the twelve warmest years on record since the beginning of consistent global surface temperature ratings in 1850. ₁

As the global temperature rises, our climate becomes more erratic. At the same time, glaciers are melting around the world, releasing water into the oceans ' and contributing to rising sea levels. As climate change continues to escalate, we will see more extreme weather, more

greenpeace
living

greenpeace

ecosystem disruption, more species extinction and other disastrous consequences for humans and the environment.

Individual emissions account for about 24 percent of Canada's total greenhouse gas emissions. [2] That means you can have a real impact on Canada's contribution to climate change. In fact, reducing energy use is one of the few green steps you will take that can be measured in concrete terms. Check your energy bill every month after implementing some of these tips—it will go down.

While it's critical for individuals to take responsibility for climate change, as with all environmental issues, the real answer is strong government regulation. It's up to all of us to make climate change an issue in every election.

Fact:

Canadians are some of the highest per capita energy users in the world. Canada is responsible for 2 percent of global greenhouse gas emissions. [3]

Must read:

Natural Resources Canada's Office of Energy Efficiency lists energy-efficient appliances and explains in detail how to retrofit your home for energy efficiency. Go to: www.oee.nrcan.gc.ca

Where to start:

* If you own your home, use caulking and weather stripping to plug air leaks; upgrade your insulation for walls, basement and attic; install an energy-efficient furnace and energy-efficient windows and choose a programmable thermostat. (See safety note.)

* Take advantage of rebates available for your energy efficiency measures at: www.oee.nrcan.gc.ca

* If you have access to your thermostat, turn down the heat at night and when you go out.

ENERGY (AT HOME)

* Choose major appliances including refrigerators, dishwashers, dryers, clothing washers and window air-conditioning units with an ENERGY STAR rating.

* Use compact fluorescent light bulbs (and make sure to read safety instructions).

* Eat fewer meat and animal products (vegetarian diets generate fewer greenhouse gas emissions) and choose food from local producers.

* Ask your energy provider if you can switch to renewable energy sources.

* Demand renewable energy sources and coherent climate policies from provincial and federal governments.

Individual vs. per capita emissions

Annual individual emissions for one Canadian resident: approximately 5.7 tonnes
Average per capita emissions for one Canadian resident: approximately 23 tonnes

According to the federal government's 2005 statistics, each individual Canadian produces 5.7 tonnes of greenhouse gases annually. That statistic is based on your personal emissions—road transportation, heating and cooling, water heating, appliances and lighting. These individual emissions make up approximately 24 percent of Canada's greenhouse gas emissions. The rest comes from industry (especially the energy industry), agriculture, land clearing and commercial transportation. If you take Canada's 2005 emissions and divide them by the population, our per capita emissions are considerably higher, almost twenty-three tonnes of greenhouse gases each. That makes Canadians some of the highest per capita energy emitters in the world. [4]

Want more?

1. Retrofit.

Retrofitting can mean a number of different things—anything from a top to bottom energy overhaul to some fine tuning around the edges. Here are a few concrete ways you can remake your home to reduce energy waste. (If you rent an apartment and are subject to the whims of your landlord, barred from adjusting the thermostat and stuck with drafty old windows, read on in this section for ways you can make your home more energy-efficient without significant investment.)

✳ Caulk and weather strip to plug air leaks. Caulking and weather stripping can save you up to 20 percent on your heating bill. You can have an airtight home and still get fresh air without losing heat by installing an air-to-air heat exchanger. Proper ventilation is necessary for health and safety. Consult an expert.

For information on how to control air leaks from Natural Resources Canada, see: www.oee.nrcan.gc.ca

✳ Upgrade your insulation. Improving the insulation in your walls, basement and attic can reduce your heating bill by up to 30 percent.

✳ Choose energy-efficient windows and doors. Drafty windows can be responsible for up to 25 percent of heat loss in homes. Replace single-glazed windows with double- or triple-glazed windows. Old external doors should be replaced with insulated core doors and/or storm doors.

✳ Install a programmable thermostat and set it to automatically lower at least three degrees Celsius at night and while you're out.

✳ Turn down your hot water heater. Many Canadian hot water heaters are set around 60 degrees Celsius—hot enough to cause severe burns. According to the Canadian Health Network, hot waters heaters should be set no higher (and, for health reasons, no lower) than

49 degrees Celsius. Please note that, according to Safe Kids Canada: "This option is not recommended for homes with the current design of electric storage water tanks or with a household member who has a risk factor for legionnaires' disease (such as respiratory problems or a weak immune system)."

For more information from Safe Kids Canada, visit: www.sickkids.ca

* Get rid of your electric heating. Due to energy losses during generation, transmission and end-use, electricity is the least efficient way to provide water and space heating. Furnaces and water heaters that use solar power or that burn fossil fuels directly produce fewer greenhouse gas emissions and other pollutants than those that use electricity. This also applies to the use of electricity for cooking and drying clothes.

* Install solar hot water. Solar hot water uses heat from sunlight for both hot water and space heating and can provide at least 50 percent of hot water needs (you will still need a back-up conventional water heater for use in winter). Solar hot water heating is effective, cost-efficient and a great way to cut down on your energy bills.

For more information about how to install a solar hot water system in your home, visit the Canadian Solar Industries Association at: www.cansia.ca

* Install photovoltaic solar panels. Photovoltaic solar panels can be installed to generate electricity directly for household use. Photovoltaic panels can be used off the grid for homes in remote locations (you will need to invest in a battery system). They can also be connected to the grid, reducing your electricity use but allowing you to continue using utility power.

For more details on photovoltaic solar panels, visit the Canadian Solar Industries Association at: www.cansia.ca

For more energy-saving home improvement tips, visit: www.oee.rncan.gc.ca

Take advantage of rebates available for your energy efficiency measures at: www.oee.nrcan.gc.ca

2. Turn down your thermostat (especially when you're out).

If you reduce your thermostat by one degree Celsius, you can reduce your energy consumption by 2 percent.

3. Choose energy-efficient appliances.

Products displaying the ENERGY STAR logo are among the most efficient on the market, typically 10 to 50 percent better than conventional models. Choose major appliances including refrigerators, dishwashers, dryers, clothing washers and window air-conditioning units with an ENERGY STAR rating. ENERGY STAR also certifies products for heating, cooling and ventilation.

For a list of ENERGY STAR-rated appliances, visit: www.oee.nrcan.gc.ca

4. Choose compact fluorescent light bulbs.

Replace old-fashioned incandescent bulbs with compact fluorescent light bulbs (CFLs). Compact fluorescents use 75 percent less energy and last ten times longer than incandescent light bulbs. A typical seventy-five watt incandescent bulb can be replaced by a twenty watt compact fluorescent bulb. CFLs are more expensive at the outset but they typically last five years (assuming you use them for about three hours per day) and can save about thirty dollars a year each in electricity charges.

Take some simple precautions when using CFLs. Don't use them in closed fixtures (like globes or covered, recessed fixtures) because the ballast may overheat. Do not use with dimmers—this creates a fire hazard. (There are some new CFLs available.you can use on dimmers but they are expensive and hard to find. This must be explicitly stated on the package.) Check the packages for safety warnings and compatibility with different kinds of fixtures.

For more information from Natural Resources Canada on CFLs, visit: www.oee.nrcan.gc.ca

At the end of their operating life, CFLs should be disposed of properly so the mercury inside can be recycled. To find out how to safely dispose of CFLs, contact your municipality.

5. Reduce stand-by energy consumption.

Most modern electrical appliances consume electricity even when turned off—this is called stand-by time. In the year 2000, the European Union lost ninety-four billion kilowatt hours to stand-by, the equivalent of twelve large nuclear or coal plants. ₅

Choose appliances with very low stand-by energy consumption—this will be listed in the product manual or on some manufacturer websites. According to Greenpeace International, stand-by consumption for most appliances should be between 0.5 and one watt per hour or between four and eight kilowatt hours per year. Remember—the cost of wasted stand-by energy over a product's lifetime can be higher than the cost of the item itself.

A good way to reduce stand-by consumption: keep groups of electronics (like your computer and printer, for example) on one power bar and switch it off when you're done. Just make sure the outlet can handle it.

6. Add up household efficiencies.

Make laundry energy-efficient. Wash your clothes in cold water whenever possible (this will save energy and also help to extend the life of many garments). Avoid using the dryer if you can—they are usually extremely energy-intensive. Hang your clothes up to dry. Replace old washers and dryers with ENERGY STAR rated models. Efficient washers should cut down on water usage as well.

Make your kitchen energy-efficient. There are lots of small ways to reduce your energy use in the kitchen. An electric kettle uses less energy than a stove-top model. Cover the pot when heating water—it will boil faster. Replace old refrigerators with ENERGY STAR rated models and never leave the fridge door open for more than a few seconds. Composting also fights global warming by helping to keep organic waste out of landfills where it produces methane, a powerful greenhouse gas.

Make your bathroom energy-efficient. In the bathroom, the best way to save on energy costs is to cut down on hot water use. Install aerators on taps and water-saving shower heads.

Make use of passive solar. Throw open the curtains in the winter during the day. The sun will help heat your home. In the summer, draw the curtains to keep things cooler (but make sure to let in the breeze if you're not using air-conditioning).

7. Find food energy savings.

Meat-based diets require huge inputs of energy. According to researchers at the University of Chicago, the average American meat-based diet generates approximately 1.5 tonnes of greenhouse gas emissions more per year than a vegetarian diet. [6]

The United Nations Food and Agriculture Organization estimates that, globally, livestock are now responsible for more greenhouse gas emissions than transportation. [7]

Buying locally grown and processed food can also help to cut down on greenhouse gas emissions from transportation. Try eating within your season as much as possible, avoiding food like berries, for example, in the winter.

8. Choose green energy.

Purchasing green electricity can be a good way to reduce your greenhouse gas emissions and encourage the development of renewable energy like wind and solar power. Ask your energy provider if you have the option to purchase green energy. Unfortunately, your options will be dictated by the regulatory regime, energy matrix and private entrepreneurs in your province—there is no federal plan in place for regulating access to renewable energy.

It's also important to note that some green energy plans can be

ENERGY (AT HOME)

largely metaphorical. Often, when you are 'buying' green energy, it's not necessarily going directly to power your home. Find out whether the electricity is being fed into the grid on your behalf.

For excellent information about carbon offset and renewable energy programs in Canada from the David Suzuki Foundation, please visit: www.davidsuzuki.org

9. Consider carbon offsets.

Carbon offset programs allow you to, in effect, do something good to compensate for doing something bad. Taking a flight? Calculate the

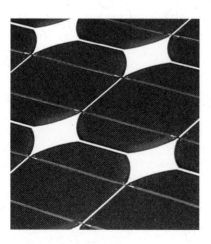

climate damage and buy the equivalent amount of wind power. Going on a road trip? Have some trees planted on your behalf.

While there are obvious problems with this formulation—the best environmental bet is to reduce energy use, not compensate for it—carbon offset programs can be a good way to deal with your unavoidable emissions and encourage the development of green energy.

Please note: not all carbon offset programs are created equal. Some, like tree-planting programs for example, may not be effective if the trees die or are cut down after a few years. Carbon offset programs are unregulated so make sure to carefully research the program you choose.

10. **Demand renewable energy sources and comprehensive emissions reductions programs from provincial and federal governments.**

Canada is not doing enough to curb its greenhouse gas emissions. The federal government needs to dramatically increase funding for both energy efficiency measures and renewable energy programs.

The government also needs to discontinue subsidies to dirty energy sources like fossil fuels and nuclear power. In Alberta, the tar sands—which generate five times more greenhouse gas emissions than conventional oil extraction—have, up until recently, received a 100 percent capital cost write-off. Similarly, nuclear power, which produces deadly, long-living radioactive waste, receives about $200 million per year in public subsidies. [8]

Eliminating subsidies to conventional energy and transferring them to green energy technologies—like wind and solar energy—would be a good first step in Canada's fight against climate change.

Contact federal and provincial governments and demand aggressive climate policies that promote green energy, develop energy efficiency, end subsidies to conventional energy and mandate strong emissions standards for cars.

Safety note:

While sealing warm and cold air into your home will improve your overall energy efficiency, you must consider circulation and ventilation. If you do not have proper ventilation, this poses a health risk.

Governments must adopt aggressive policies that promote renewable energy like wind and solar power.

greenpeace
living

greenpeace

FLOOR COVERINGS

OVERVIEW

Flooring touches on environmental issues from toxics to forest preservation to labour practices. Some flooring is made from unsustainably logged wood from ancient forests like the Amazon. Other flooring is made from the toxic plastic polyvinyl chloride (PVC). But the flooring material itself is only part of the issue—adhesives, dyes, sealers and preservatives used to treat and fix floor coverings can be serious contributors to indoor air pollution. Luckily, a bouquet of functional, beautiful and time-tested environmentally friendly options is out there for green shoppers right now!

Fact:

According to Public Works and Government Services Canada, vinyl gives off by far the greatest amount of emissions of any common floor covering. [1]

Where to start:

* Choose flooring made from renewable resources like linoleum, cork and bamboo.

* For wood flooring, choose reclaimed over new wood.

* Choose carpets made from natural materials like wool, sea grass and hemp.

* Choose wood flooring certified by the Forest Stewardship Council or the Rainforest Alliance.

* Avoid flooring made from polyvinyl chloride or endangered wood.

* Avoid synthetic carpets made from petrochemicals.

* Avoid flooring, carpets and under padding treated with hazardous chemicals.

Want more?

AVOID

Polyvinyl chloride (PVC). PVC has rapidly replaced linoleum as a source of common, non-ceramic floor tiles. PVC is a highly polluting plastic at every stage of its lifecycle from manufacturing to consumer use to disposal. It does not biodegrade, off-gasses toxic chemicals and contains chlorine, which will emit dioxins both during processing and combustion.

For more information about PVC, visit: www.pvcinformation.org

CHOOSE

Before the 1950s craze for synthetic materials ushered in the era of PVC, linoleum dominated the flooring market. Linoleum, which comes in both sheet and tile options, is made from renewable resources including vegetable linseed, natural resin and cork powder. It's highly durable and can be washed with natural soaps and water.

Some linoleums, however, are treated with toxic sealers, waxes and other finishings. For example, although they have been eliminated by most manufacturers, lead monoxide or red lead (both poisons) may be used as driers. Ask specific questions about how linoleum is treated and about any off-gassing concerns.

Other washable flooring options include ceramic tile (some of which is now being manufactured with some recycled glass content) and terrazzo. As with all flooring, make sure to check on the adhesives and treatments.

For more information visit: www.healthybuilding.net

AVOID

Products made from unsustainable, illegally logged and endangered wood. Avoid tropical wood that is not Forest Stewardship Council certified. In addition, think about the transportation fuel costs of getting flooring from the other side of the planet. Plywood and particleboard, which can be treated with formaldehyde, should also be avoided. For more information, please see 'Wood.'

CHOOSE

Reclaimed and/or Forest Stewardship Council (FSC) certified wood. The Forest Stewardship Council (FSC) certifies wood that comes from logging operations that are socially and environmentally responsible. This means that environmental concerns are respected and that communities are consulted and considered. FSC is the only certification system broadly recognized by non-governmental environmental organizations like Greenpeace. FSC certified wood is available for a number of purposes, including flooring. Like linoleum, even FSC certified wood can later be treated with toxics.

While FSC certification generally applies to newly logged wood, the Rainforest Alliance has developed a label for reclaimed wood (which can come from old buildings, found logs, dead trees and post-consumer sources) called 'Rediscovered Wood.' This certification system monitors the process used to recover, recycle and reuse wood according to social and environmental criteria including cultural considerations, the handling of chemicals and worker safety.

For more information and a list of distributors, visit: www.fsccanada.org

For more information on the 'Rediscovered Wood' label, visit: www.rainforest-alliance.org

AVOID

Synthetic carpets and hazardous treatments. Synthetic carpets are usually made from petrochemicals, a non-renewable resource. Many carpets are also treated with moth-proofing, stain protection and other chemical treatments that can off-gas volatile organic compounds (VOCs). Contact your carpet manufacturer to find out more about their chemicals policy. Ask if they have a program in place to substitute known hazardous chemicals with safer substitutes.

CHOOSE

Choose carpets made from wool, cotton (preferably organic), jute, sisal, sea grass and hemp. Make sure to pay attention to under pads and carpet-backings as well. Always ask suppliers what kind of chemical treatments have been applied to your carpets. Used carpets can be a good option, especially when they fit into the criteria described above. You can also consider modular carpets that let you build your carpet square by square. That way, you only need to replace the specific sections that are worn down or stained. Even some of the more sustainable carpet options can off-gas within the first few days of installation. Make sure to ventilate areas with newly-installed carpets.

For help choosing carpeting and other flooring materials, visit the federal government's 'Environmental Choice' website at: www.environmentalchoice.com

The 'Rugmark' symbol, founded in Germany, was designed to certify that carpets produced in India, Pakistan and Nepal are woven without the use of child labour. Although some criticism has been levelled against the Rugmark label—including the fact that it fails to address some of the root causes of child labour—it has been generally credited with helping to reduce the use of child labour in some areas. [2]

For more information, visit: www.rugmark.org

More green options:

Cork sheeting and tiles are made from cork dust, a waste product from the bottle cork manufacturing industry. The cork itself comes from the outer layer of cork oak trees. Cork is hard-wearing and sound absorbent. Cork floor coverings are available with untreated or sealed surfaces. Artificial resins (polyurethane) or PVC sealants should be avoided.

Bamboo is a fast-growing, renewable resource that can be milled into beautiful hardwood-style planks. Bamboo flooring and

FLOOR COVERINGS

carpet is widely available. Look for sustainable bamboo that wasn't grown at the expense of natural forests. And, as with all flooring, check to make sure surface treatments and adhesives are low or no-VOC.

For more information and suggestions from the Safer Products Project, visit: www.saferproducts.org

For more information on flooring from Public Works and Government Services Canada, visit: www.pwgsc.gc.ca

Right: Choose Forest Stewardship Council certified wood. Visit www.fsccanada.org for more information.

FOOD

OVERVIEW

The food we choose impacts the environment in countless ways. Globally, industrial food production uses staggering amounts of water and energy, releases toxic chemicals into the environment and contributes to the loss of biodiversity (the variety of plants and animals on the planet).

The advent of genetically engineered (GE) foods over the past decade has created a new form of pollution— genetic contamination. Genetic engineering (in concert with current regulatory systems in countries including Canada and the US) has also helped to consolidate corporate control over the global food supply.

Must read:

Stolen Harvest: the hijacking of the global food supply by Vandana Shiva. South End Press. 2000. *The Omnivore's Dilemma,* by Michael Pollan. Penguin Press. 2006.

Must see:

El Contrato - Min Sook Lee's excellent documentary on farm workers in Ontario's tomato industry. For more information, visit: www.nfb.ca

Fact:

Approximately 70 percent of processed foods in Canadian grocery stores contain GE ingredients. [1] 91 percent of GE crops planted in the world come from one American company— Monsanto. [2] In Canada, the federal government currently has only voluntary labelling legislation in place to compel manufacturers to label GE food. No GE food labels have been found in Canada to date, proving that we need the kind of mandatory labelling rules already in place in more than forty countries around the world.

Where to start:

✻ Eat plant-based meals whenever possible.

✻ Avoid genetically engineered ingredients.

✻ Choose locally produced, certified organic foods.

✻ Choose unprocessed foods.

✻ Choose fair trade certified products.

✻ Reduce food waste—only buy what you will eat.

✻ Buy in bulk and bring your own bags and containers to the store.

✻ Grow your own food at home or at a community garden.

✻ Ask store managers to stock organic, local, fair trade certified products.

✻ Reduce seafood consumption and avoid toxic and endangered fish.

Simple step:

Try introducing one purely plant-based meal a week (that means no meat, no seafood and no dairy) and go from there as you become more comfortable with vegetarian cooking. Work your way up until you are going one day per week without animal products. After that, as an experiment, try a whole week. A good way to get started: try one new vegetarian recipe each month. Slowly but surely, your repertoire will grow.

Visit www.vegcooking.com for recipes and resources.

FOOD

Want more?

1. Avoid genetically engineered (GE) food.

Genetic engineering allows corporations to insert genes from one organism into another, unrelated organism. The results are not found in nature and cannot be achieved by traditional cross-breeding techniques.

GE crops are usually sold by multinational corporations and are often designed to survive repeated applications of specific, patented weed- or pest-killing chemical formulations. For example, Monsanto's Roundup

Ready soybeans are resistant to Monsanto's Roundup herbicide, so farmers buy both their seeds and their chemicals from Monsanto.

While there are many environmental risks associated with GE food, the consequences for human health are still unknown. Even though GE food has been in grocery stores for more than ten years, there have been no long-term tests done on the impacts of GE food on human health.

In Canada, common GE crops include corn, soy, canola and cottonseed. Today, approximately 70 percent of processed foods in Canadian grocery stores contain GE ingredients. The Canadian regulatory system does not require GE food to be labelled and few (if any) food manufacturers have taken advantage of the weak voluntary labelling regime that is now in place.

To avoid GE foods, read the ingredients on non-organic processed foods. If they contain corn, soy, canola or cottonseed oil or their derivatives, chances are they contain GE ingredients. Industrially produced corn, in particular, is ubiquitous in North American processed foods (and consumer goods) and is used to make a dizzying array of additives.

Fresh fruits and vegetables in Canada are generally not genetically engineered. Some exceptions include papayas imported from the US and possibly corn. Unfortunately, there is no way to tell whether or not you are looking at a GE papaya or a traditional papaya unless, of course, you are buying organic. Organic products and produce are not allowed to contain GE ingredients.

2. Choose organics.

Try to increase your consumption of organic food as much as you can. Organic food is GE-free—it is also grown without synthetic pesticides and fertilizers. There are a number of third party certifiers in Canada who certify products as organic. Look for certified organic food at the grocery store and at farmer's markets. There is also an increasing number of organic home delivery services—many offer organic foods at competitive prices. Try searching the internet for one in your area.

All kinds of foods are certified organic, not just fresh produce. Look for dairy, meat and processed foods as well. Certified organic foods can be more expensive than conventional produce but try and substitute them as often as you can. As the market for organic food grows, prices will continue to go down.

For information on where to buy organic food in Canada, visit: www.cog.ca/buyorganic.htm and www.eatwellguide.org

3. Eat low on the food chain.

More resources are required to produce a meal of meat and animal by-products (like cheese and milk) than to produce a meal of unprocessed vegetables and grain. Vast amounts of grain must be fed to cattle, for example, to produce even a small amount of animal protein for human consumption. According to the Worldwatch Institute, the total amount of soy and grain fed to livestock in the US each year could feed everyone on the planet approximately five times over. [3]

Currently, food agencies are drawing a correlation between food shortages and meat consumption. In 2008, the United Nations World Food Programme warned it lacked the resources to keep up with rising food prices which it attributed to a number of factors including climate change, biofuels and increased demand for animal feed. [4]

Meat and animal products don't just waste other food sources. They use massive amounts of water and energy as well. While estimates vary, researchers at the University of Chicago calculate that if an average, meat-eating American switched to a plant-based diet, they would eliminate approximately 1.5 tonnes of greenhouse gas emissions each year. [5] (For scale, recent statistics put Canadian per capita greenhouse gas emissions at about twenty-three tonnes per year.) In addition, animal products—in particular grain-fed beef—require significantly more water than cereals like corn, wheat, barley and oats. [6]

Meat cultivation also chews through forests at a breakneck pace. According to the United Nations Food and Agriculture Organization, livestock production now accounts for 30 percent of the planet's surface area (including both grazing areas and arable land used to grow crops for feed). [7] In Brazil and Argentina, areas of the Amazon have been cleared to grow soy, much of it for animal feed in Europe. In 2004-2005, around 1.2 million hectares of soy were planted in the Brazilian Amazon alone. [8] In addition to consuming resources, feed lots on factory farms can contribute to water pollution.

Cut out animal products or make a formal plan to cut down. If you are going to buy meat, poultry and animal by-products, buy local and organic.

4. Choose local.

While organic food is almost always the best choice, you should also consider where and by whom it was grown. Many smaller organic producers have been bought out by big conglomerates which then apply some of the basic tenets of industrial agriculture to organic farming. Locally grown food is easier to trace to small, responsible producers, especially when you buy it from a farmers' market, a food co-op or from Community Supported Agriculture. In addition, local food doesn't need to be transported as far so it generates fewer greenhouse gas emissions. For fun, challenge yourself to eat a '100-mile diet' for a few days—choose food that has been grown within a 100-mile radius of your home.

The best case scenario for the environment is, of course, food that is both organic and locally grown. Sometimes, you're going to have to weigh your options and make a choice. Support local farmers' markets and food co-ops. Consider ordering a weekly organic produce basket. Buy fresh, organic produce in season. Community Supported Agriculture (CSA) is another good option for green eaters. CSA allows you to pre-buy—in essence, invest—in a farmer's annual crop. The dividends: farm fresh food, as soon as it's ripe.

To find a local CSA, try an internet search or ask at your local food co-op.

For tips on how to follow a '100-mile diet,' visit: www.100milediet.org

5. Choose unprocessed.

Less processing and less packaging most often means less pollution, fewer chemical additives and more nutritious food. Choose fresh produce, bulk cereals and grains and fresh dairy products. Staying away from non-organic processed foods is also a great way to avoid GE ingredients.

6. Choose fair trade and demand rights for agricultural workers in Canada.

Fair trade is one way of attempting to pay the real cost of food and to develop some integrity in

relationships with producers and products. Common fair trade food products available in Canada include cocoa products, coffee, tea, sugar and fresh fruit. Support fair trade and rights for agricultural workers in Canada and around the world.

For more information on agricultural workers in Canada, visit: www.justicia4migrantworkers.org

For more information on fair trade products available in Canada, visit: www.transfair.ca

7. Choose seafood carefully.
See the section 'Seafood.'

8. Grow something.

Try growing your own food. You'd be surprised what you can do with a balcony, a small patch of land or a window sill. This is a great way to access organics at lower prices. It will also cut out the greenhouse gases commonly needed to transport food from field to table. Try borrowing a book on organic gardening from your·local library and take it from there. Many municipalities also have community gardens. Contact them early in the year to reserve space for your own, personal mini-crop. If there's no existing community garden in your area, consider getting together with your neighbours and starting your own.

For links to community gardens across Canada, visit: www.communitygarden.org/links.php

9. Avoid excess packaging.
Avoid toxic packaging.

There is an obvious hierarchy of packaging options. The best case scenario: no package at all.

Bring your own bags to the grocery store and—if the store lets you—fill up your own containers with bulk items. Look for packaging that is recycled and recyclable.

Avoid plastic packaging whenever possible and take particular care to avoid food items packaged in:

✳ Polystyrene plastic—foam packaging usually labelled with a #6.

✳ Polyvinyl chloride plastic, also known as PVC and usually labelled with a #3.

✳ Polycarbonate plastic—hard, clear plastic usually labelled with a #7. (Unfortunately, some food cans are also coated with polycarbonate plastics.)

(See the 'Plastics' section for more information about plastic and food.)

10. Ask for what you want.

Ask store managers to stock the products you are looking for. Be polite but assertive. Request a range of local organic meat, dairy, produce and processed foods. Demand fair trade products like coffee, tea and chocolate.

Consider asking public institutions such as schools, libraries and government offices to adopt organic purchasing policies—the more demand for organics, the better for everyone.

PACKAGING

OVERVIEW

Packaging is a category that touches on almost every single product listed in this guide. It's also a category that dovetails nicely with our old nemesis, the one that pops up in your moisturizer, your soup can and your underwear. That's right: petroleum. Almost all plastics currently on the market are made from petroleum products. And many of the rest of them—the ones marketed as a miracle substitute for a post-petroleum world—are made with genetically engineered (GE) corn. Leaving aside for the moment the

madness of diverting *food* for use in disposable containers, GE corn is not the answer to sustainable packaging. GE corn requires large inputs of agricultural chemicals, swathes of arable land and, perhaps most disturbingly, its DNA is owned by corporations like Monsanto.

So single-use, throw away plastic is out. That brings us to the second, broad category of packaging: materials made from wood pulp like cardboard and paper. Unfortunately, sometimes that wood pulp comes from ancient, irreplaceable forests. Post-consumer recycled wood-pulp materials are available, but this is not a real answer to our packaging problem. Post-consumer recycled plastic materials are available too, but, again, not a real answer. The answer is, of course, is to revisit the idea of packaging itself.

Fact:

According to Daniel Imhoff's book, *Paper or Plastic?*, more than 150 billion single-use beverage containers are sold in the US each year.

Where to start:

✳ Choose reusable cloth bags for grocery shopping.

✳ Buy items in bulk and in concentrate.

✳ Carry a reusable mug for coffee.

✳ If you can, say goodbye to bottled water.

✳ Avoid take-out containers. Try bringing your own reusable containers into local businesses instead.

✳ Choose packaging that is both post-consumer recycled and recyclable.

✳ Research recycling rules for your area.

✳ Reuse, pass on, compost or recycle all packaging.

✳ Ask retailers and manufacturers to offer bulk items and take responsibility for used packages like empty bottles and lipstick tubes. Consider de-nuding your purchase right there at the store and asking the manager to dispose of the packaging for you.

Simple step:

Try packing garbage-free lunches for you and your family. Start by avoiding juice boxes, straws, pre-packaged snacks, plastic cutlery, paper napkins and plastic bags. Replace with a reusable lunch box, real cutlery, chopsticks, cloth napkins and a thermos. Bring home leftover food items for compost. Consider organizing a monthly waste-free lunch day at school or work.

PACKAGING

Want more?

1. Create a shopping kit.

Preparation is the key to a green life. Keep a collapsible cloth bag with you for impulse purchases. For bigger, organized shopping trips, create a little shopping kit. Make it practical and loveable, something you'll use over and over again. Make sure it includes a few cloth bags and some clean, reusable food-safe containers. Some stores will let you use your own containers for bulk items from shampoo to almonds. And every store will let you use your cloth bags—some even offer financial incentives.

2. Create a take-out kit.

A kit is always a good thing. It helps you establish habits and invest (time and creativity—not necessarily money) in the decision you've made to green your life. Carrying your own, reusable travel coffee mug is an easy way to start reducing your packaging misdemeanours. For more elaborate take-out propositions (like dinner), try asking a few of your favourite restaurants and delis if you can bring in your own, food-safe, reusable take-out containers. Many places will be amenable to this. Some serious neighbourhood spots will even let you take their plates or containers home as long as you make sure to bring them back.

3. Choose bulk.

Here's where you will really start to save money. Most stores—even large chains—offer nuts, dried beans, candy and other items in bulk. Buying large amounts helps cut down on costs, number of shopping trips and packaging. But remember: never buy more than you need, especially when dealing with perishable items. Some health food stores and food co-ops will also sell cleaners, shampoo and a larger variety of food items in bulk. Find out if your local store will let you bring in reusable containers for loose bulk items. Buying items like laundry soap in concentrated form can also help to cut down on packaging.

4. Be picky about packaging.

Okay, so you can't stick it in your own container or put it directly in your cloth bag. Now what? Well, first ask yourself if the product is over-packaged. Avoid individually packaged items like juice boxes, for example. And stay away from the pure madness of blister-packed gum or magazines that come in their own, individual plastic baggies.

Once you've established that the product's packaging isn't straight up egregious, figure out what it's made of. If it's cardboard or plastic, does it have post-consumer recycled content?

And can it be recycled in your area? Once you've created a permanent packaging hierarchy in your head, it will be easy to scan the aisles for the vessel of your dreams.

5. Research recycling.

Take an afternoon, go to your municipality's website or give them a call, and figure out exactly what you can recycle.

Most programs accept #1 and #2 plastics, glass, newspapers and cardboard—but what else? Get a list of recycling categories and tack it up on the fridge. Then, when you're in the grocery store, avoid packaging you know will end up in the landfill.

6. Demand coherent solutions.

Whether we use petroleum, corn or purple loosestrife to make our packaging, there simply aren't enough resources available to keep us in juice boxes forever. The solution: governments need to start enforcing Individual Producer Responsibility. And they have. Jurisdictions including Bangladesh, South Africa, Australia, Shanghai and, most recently, Leaf Rapids in Manitoba, all have bans or levies in place on plastic bags. In Ireland, a fifteen cent surcharge cut down plastic bag use by 90 percent and generated millions of dollars in revenue for the government. ₁ Finland requires all take-out drinks and alcohol to be packaged in returnable bottles. In Germany, manufacturers pay advance recycling fees and are

rewarded with a green dot symbol on their products.

Bottom line: there should be a relationship between the cost of the product and the amount of resources it takes to produce and dispose of it. Too often, product costs are 'externalized,' sparing producers and consumers costs while forcing workers, communities and the planet to take the hit. It is possible and practical to require suppliers to deal with their leftovers.

Ask the federal and provincial governments to implement Individual Producer Responsibility—some provincial governments in Canada already have.

Choose one or two suppliers and tell them that you want them to take responsibility for their packaging. Fill out a customer comment card or send an email. Make sure they know consumers want (and will reward) change.

For more information on Individual Producer Responsibility from the federal government, visit: www.ec.gc.ca

PAINTS, FINISHES AND ADHESIVES

OVERVIEW

You know that fresh paint smell? Well, it's a bad thing. It's produced when the toxic volatile organic compounds (VOCs) used as solvents in many paints, paint strippers, glues and varnishes off-gas into the air. The VOCs contained in some types of paint, coatings and strippers include known carcinogens and neurotoxins. [1] They are also harmful to the environment, particularly if disposed of incorrectly. According to Pollution Probe, paints and coatings are the biggest source of VOCs attributable to solvent use. [2] The good news: there are alternatives.

Fact:

According to the Environmental Protection Agency in the US, the levels of some VOCs can be up to 1,000 times higher indoors after activities like paint stripping. [3]

Must read:

For detailed information on paints and finishes from Public Works and Government Services Canada, visit the *Environmentally Responsible Construction and Renovation Handbook* at: www.pwgsc.gc.ca

Where to start:

* Avoid solvent-based paints.

* Choose products with the lowest volatile organic compound (VOC) content you can find. (Or better yet, if you can find them, choose VOC-free paints and finishes.)

* Explore paints made from natural ingredients, like old-fashioned milk paints.

Want more?

1. **Avoid VOCs and heavy metals in paint, glue, sealants and finishes.**

Petrochemical solvents are used in paint and coatings to help disperse the other ingredients. After the paint or coating has been applied, the solvents off-gas, releasing toxic chemicals in the form of VOCs into the air. As a basic rule, avoid solvent-based paints—often called oil or alkyd paints—completely.

That leaves you with several options. The first is water-based, latex paint. Opt for latex paints labelled low-VOC or, ideally, no-VOC. Look for paint, glue, varnishes and treatments with the lowest VOC content you can find—this is often listed on the label as grams per litre. Please note that even paints labelled 'low-VOC' have been found to off-gas toxic chemicals including formaldehyde. 4

Your next option: when possible, choose paints made from natural ingredients, like old-fashioned milk paints. Make sure you choose the right paint for the right room—some natural paints could mildew and might not work in the kitchen or the bathroom.

For finishes, linseed oil and beeswax can be good options for wood (it's a good idea to get some expert help when treating wood and other surfaces).

Remember—even natural paints can emit VOCs. No matter what kind of paint you are using, ventilate the room for a few days after painting or when using varnish, coatings or strong glues. Public Works and Government Services Canada also recommends the use of facemasks or respirators when applying paints and other coverings. Pregnant women and children should stay away from paint, varnish, coatings and other VOC-emitting products. When working with toxic substances, it's always good to get expert help.

Some paints and coatings are endorsed by Environment Canada's Environmental

Choice program (visit www.environmentalchoice.com to search by product). Take a moment to read their criteria for each product.

2. Watch out for lead paint in older buildings.

Buildings constructed before the 1960s are likely to contain lead paint. Buildings constructed before 1980 might also contain lead paint. Homes built before the early nineties could have lead paint on the outside. ₅

Removing old paint is potentially hazardous. Lead paint can also be hazardous if it's chipping, peeling, chalking, cracking or in high-traffic areas used frequently by children like doors, door frames, window sills, stairs, banisters, porches and fences.

Lead exposure is a very serious health hazard, particularly for children. If you think you have lead paint in your home, school or workplace, seek expert advice.

To read a Health Canada fact sheet on lead-based paint, visit: www.hc-sc.gc.ca

Environment Canada recommends contacting your local branch of the Canada Mortgage and Housing Corporation for instructions on how to remove and dispose of lead paint: www.cmhc-schl.gc.ca

3. Dispose of hazardous substances properly.

Do not throw paint, varnishes, coatings, sealants or glue down the drain or out with your regular garbage pick-up. Generally, even 'natural' paints should be disposed of as hazardous substances.

Contact your municipality to find out about their hazardous waste disposal programs. Store all hazardous substances—including natural paints, coatings, sealants, glues and varnishes—safely out of reach of children.

Right: Do not throw paints, varnishes, coatings, sealants or glue down the drain. Contact your muncipality about hazardous waste.

PAPER AND PRINTING

OVERVIEW

Even with an increasing reliance on computers, people are using more paper, not less. Global paper consumption has more than tripled over the past thirty years. In Canada, paper production is taking a toll on ancient forests. Paper mills also produce toxic effluent which, in the past, has resulted in devastating consequences for affected communities—polluting fresh water, poisoning wildlife and making people sick. From harvesting to production, from shipping to printing, the paper industry has a serious impact on people and the environment.

Must read:

For excellent resources on ancient forest friendly paper, visit: www.marketsinitiative.org and www.ancientforestfriendly.com. For information on forest-friendly tissue products, visit: http://tissue.greenpeace.ca

Fact:

71 percent of the world's paper supply comes from ecologically valuable, biologically diverse forests. [1]

Where to start:

* Buy only 100 percent post-consumer recycled paper and/or paper that is Forest Stewardship Council certified.

* Reduce paper use at home and at work.

* Always recycle.

* Choose tissue products, books, magazines and packaging that are recycled and/or FSC certified.

* Choose paper and packaging that is processed chlorine-free (PCF) or totally chlorine-free (TCF).

Want more?

1. Use less paper.

Here are a few easy steps to reduce your paper use:

AT HOME:

✳ Put a 'PLEASE NO UNADDRESSED MAIL' sign up in front of your mailbox.

✳ Print on both sides of every page.

✳ Share magazines and books with friends instead of buying your own copies.

✳ Make pads out of scrap paper for taking messages and making lists.

✳ If you have a computer and access to the internet, do more of your reading online and less on paper. Review documents on your computer instead of printing them out. Consider giving up your newspaper and getting your news online.

✳ Get off mailing lists: https://cornerstonewebmedia.com /cma/submit.asp

✳ Choose products with recycled and FSC certified packaging.

✳ Opt for durable, reusable dishes and real glassware for picnics, birthday parties and BBQs.

AT WORK:

✳ Ask a technician to make double-sided copying the 'default' setting on the photocopier.

✳ Reduce the paper weight you are using for photocopying, printing and offset printing— lighter paper uses less pulp.

✳ Reuse envelopes whenever possible including for inter-office mail.

✳ Reduce your print runs whenever possible—don't get stuck with extra reports you don't need.

✳ Post reports electronically.

PAPER AND PRINTING

2. Buy ancient forest friendly paper.

Excellent environmental options are available for a dizzying array of products including mailing labels, tissue products, bags and coated papers. 100 percent post-consumer recycled, processed chlorine-free paper stock is widely available and is the best choice for all paper use. Using recycled paper for all your paper needs doesn't just save trees—it reduces water and energy use as well. It also keeps paper out of landfills, where, like other waste, it releases the greenhouse gas methane as it decomposes.

Markets Initiative has created an 'Ancient Forest Friendly' label for paper that can help you choose the best paper available for your needs. You can also purchase paper that has been certified by the Forest Stewardship Certification Council (FSC). FSC certified paper contains virgin fibre sourced from logging operations that have met strict standards for social and environmental responsibility. Although there are a variety of certification bodies in Canada and around the world, the Forest Stewardship Council is the only certification endorsed by Greenpeace and most other environmental groups and has, by far, the strictest standards. Paper made from renewable resources like hemp, sugarcane and agricultural waste is also increasingly available.

For an online database of eco-friendly paper, please visit: www.marketsinitiative.org

To find out more about FSC certification and for a database of FSC certified products, please visit: www.fsccanada.org

3. Reuse and recycle.

Most municipal recycling programs accept many different types of paper and cardboard for recycling. Contact your municipality to find out what is accepted in your local program. If you don't have a comprehensive paper recycling policy at work, consider leading the way and starting one yourself. You can also donate used magazines to schools and daycares for craft projects. Even better—reuse your paper purchases. Consider sharing magazine subscriptions and other reading material with friends and neighbours.

4. Choose ancient forest friendly books and magazines.

An increasing number of publishers around the world are using ancient forest friendly paper for books, magazines and newspapers. And it all started here, in Canada, with the Markets Initiative. Working directly with publishers, the Markets Initiative has helped to spark an international movement for ancient forest friendly paper. Today, 115 Canadian book publishers and 191 magazines have committed to eliminate paper from ancient and endangered forests. [2]

For a list of forest friendly publishers, visit: www.ancientforestfriendly.com

You can also look for the FSC certified symbol and the ancient forest friendly label on books and magazines. Consider contacting your favourite newspapers and magazines to ask if they have an ancient forest friendly policy in place.

5. Careful with those tricky recycling symbols.

Just because paper has a recycling symbol doesn't mean it contains significant recycled content. Some papers and packaging labelled with a recycling symbol might contain only a small percentage of recycled fibre. The FSC symbol and/or the Ancient Forest Friendly label are both good indicators that you are buying an ancient forest friendly stock. If the product is not certified, make sure it has a high-percentage of post-consumer recycled content. (For information about recycled vs. post-consumer recycled content, see 'Tissue products.')

6. Avoid chlorine.

To make paper look white, manufacturers use bleaching processes that often include hazardous chlorine. Look for products labelled totally chlorine-free (TCF) or processed chlorine-free (PCF). Post-consumer recycled paper cannot be labelled totally chlorine-free, as it contains a variety of fibres that have already been processed—possibly with chlorine—and subsequently used by consumers. Post-consumer fibres can, however, be processed chlorine-free.

7. Choose environmentally friendly inks.

If you are involved with the printing process, ask for vegetable-based, low-VOC inks. VOCs—volatile organic compounds—are emitted as gases from products like inks, paint, glue, permanent markers and cleaning supplies and are associated with a variety of health risks.

Green business tip:

Implement an ancient forest friendly policy at work. For detailed information on how to audit suppliers, source ancient forest friendly paper and reduce paper use, please visit: www.marketsinitiative.org

To calculate the environmental impacts of different paper, visit Environmental Defense's paper calculator at: www.edf.org/papercalculator

Right: For a comprehensive database of ancient forest friendly paper, please visit: www.marketsinitiative.org

PAPER AND PRINTING

PLASTICS AND NON-STICK COATINGS

OVERVIEW

Plastics are ubiquitous. They are used to make everything from building materials to food containers to toys. Most plastics are made from non-renewable petroleum products and are treated with a variety of toxic additives to attain different properties. Since plastics are everywhere, many of the chemicals associated with plastic production, use and disposal add up in the environment and, over time, in the human body.

While our general recommendation is to find alternatives to plastics, it is important to note that some plastics are much worse than others. Many plastic containers will have numbers at the bottom surrounded by a recycling symbol. These numbers indicate the type of plastic and will help you determine what to avoid and what to recycle. In general, plastics labelled 1, 2, 4 and 5 are considered significantly safer than other plastics. Plastics labelled 3, 6 and 7 should be avoided. Unfortunately, not all plastics are labelled and sometimes you will have to call the manufacturer.

Fact:

According to the Earth Policy Institute, manufacturers use 1.5 million barrels of oil each year to produce bottles for the US bottled water market. That's enough oil to fuel approximately 100,000 cars for one year. ₁

Where to start:

✳ Avoid three of the most toxic plastics: polyvinyl chloride (PVC), polycarbonate and polystyrene (for details see 'Plastics of particular concern').

✳ Do not heat food in plastic, even in the microwave.

✳ Recycle plastic containers with your municipal waste program where possible.

✳ Bring a reusable shopping bag to the store.

✳ Do not give children PVC toys or teethers.

Want more?

1. Avoid storing food in plastic containers or plastic wrap.

In particular, do not store food in polyvinyl chloride (#3), polystyrene (#6) or polycarbonate (#7) plastics. Avoid storing oil or fatty foods in plastic. Remember to be careful when freezing glass jars—wait for food to cool before freezing and leave at least an inch of space at the top of the jar. Some types of glass should not be frozen.

2. Avoid storing water in hard plastic containers.

Avoid storing water in hard plastic pitchers. Do not use hard plastic bottles labelled with #7—they are almost always made from polycarbonate plastic. If you continue to use a polycarbonate bottle, do not use it for hot or warm liquids and discard if scratched or damaged.

3. Avoid hard plastic baby bottles and 'sippy' cups.

Hard plastics are almost always polycarbonate. Never heat liquids in polycarbonate bottles or other plastics.

4. Do not heat food or liquid in plastic containers or with plastic wrap—including in the microwave.

This includes polystyrene (foam) containers and packaged goods with grease-proof coatings like microwave popcorn. Chemicals are released from plastic when heated.

5. Always avoid PVC.

Polyvinyl chloride (PVC) is extremely toxic throughout its lifecycle from manufacturing to disposal and, because it contains chlorine, will create hazardous dioxins when burned. PVC is used to make a variety of items including plastic wrap, building materials, toys, hand bags, blinds and shower curtains.

6. Do not buy PVC toys and teethers for young children.

Unfortunately, many plastic toys are not labelled, and it's often difficult to tell whether or not

a specific item is made out of PVC. Ask the manufacturer what kind of plastic they use. In general, avoid plastic toys for young children.

To read Health Canada's advisory on young children and PVC toys, visit: www.hc-sc.gc.ca

7. Bring your own bags to the grocery store.

Shop with a reusable cloth bag or bring old bags back to the store and keep a collapsible cloth bag with you for impromptu shopping.

8. Recycle plastic.

Many plastics display a recycling symbol, but this is no guarantee that they are accepted by your local recycling program. Check with your municipality to find out which plastics are accepted. Plastic containers usually have numbers at the bottom indicating a specific type of plastic. #1, for example, indicates polyethylene terephthalate (PET) plastic. PET recycling rates are high compared to other plastics and it is usually accepted by municipal recycling programs. #2 indicates high-density polyethylene plastics which are also accepted by many recycling programs.

9. Avoid some non-stick coatings and stain-proof treatments.

Non-stick pans, grease-proof fast food wrappers and stain-resistant treatments are usually produced with perfluorochemicals, a family of substances that help repel oil and water. Some perfluorochemicals appear to be particularly toxic and bio-accumulative (meaning they have the tendency to build up in living tissues over time). They have been found in both human and wildlife populations across North America and have travelled as far from manufacturing centres as the Arctic. Perfluorochemicals have been associated with thyroid damage, cancer and the alteration of male reproductive hormones. [2] At high temperatures, non-stick cookware can release toxic chemicals into the air. According to tests commissioned by the Environmental Working Group, after less that five minutes on the stove, non-stick cookware can reach temperatures at which the coating 'breaks apart and emits toxic particles and gases linked to hundreds, perhaps thousands, of pet bird deaths and an unknown number of human illnesses each year...' [3]

While some argue that non-stick pans can be safe if used at low temperatures, everyone—including manufacturers—agree that they should never be used at high heat. If you can, replace your non-stick pans. Also make a point of avoiding microwave popcorn, which can collect significant concentrations of chemicals when heated.

For information from Health Canada on non-stick cookware, visit: www.hc-sc.gc.ca

PLASTICS AND NON-STICK COATINGS

Plastics of particular concern

Polyvinyl chloride plastic (#3)—also called PVC—is a uniquely bad plastic. It is high in chlorine and additives, and acts as an environmental poison during its entire life cycle. PVC cannot be readily recycled due to its chlorine and additive content. PVC is used to make a variety of products including blinds, shower curtains, purses and children's toys.

Polycarbonate plastic (#7) is a hard plastic used for products like reusable water bottles and CD containers. It can also be used for baby bottles and for lining food cans. Polycarbonate plastic contains bisephenol A, a chemical that mimics the female hormone estrogen. Bisephenol A is associated with a variety of health risks including low sperm counts, diabetes and prostate abnormalities. [4] Polycarbonate plastic is often labelled with a #7, although not all #7 plastics are polycarbonate. (At press time, in 2008, Canada was set to list bisephenol A as a toxic substance and become the first country in the world to ban its use for some applications.)

Polystyrene (#6) is widely used for foam insulation and consumer products like foam take-out cups and toys. Its production involves the use of known and suspected human carcinogenic substances. Styrene is also known to be toxic to the reproductive system. [5] Polystyrene can technically be recycled but recycling rates are low.

Polyurethane (PU) is mainly used in insulation and soft/foamed products like carpet underlay. It uses several hazardous intermediates and creates numerous hazardous by-products. [6]

Acrylonitrile-Butadiene-Styrene (ABS) is used as a hard plastic in products such as pipes, car bumpers and toys (hard building blocks). Acrylonitrile is highly toxic and is readily absorbed by inhalation and directly through the skin. Both the liquid and its vapor are highly toxic. Acrylonitrile is classified as a probable human carcinogen as are styrene and butadiene. [7]

A note on #7 plastics. Some manufacturers have started to work with bio-based polymers—

SEAFOOD

OVERVIEW

There is growing consensus within the scientific community that the largest single threat to marine ecosystems today is industrial fishing. New technologies are allowing industrial fishing vessels to harvest in deeper waters, generating new forms of destruction as they go and threatening smaller, local fisheries that operate closer to the coasts.

Some seafood is bottom-trawled—a fishing technique that drags a net suspended between large metal doors along the ocean floor, destroying almost everything in its wake. Some fishing techniques also result in 'by-catch'—the death of non-target ocean species that get tangled up in massive, industrial fishing nets. Add in the build-up of mercury in certain species of fish and the problems associated with some types of fish-farming and the seafood section of your grocery store can get complicated.

Fact:

Approximately 29 percent of seafood species are considered 'collapsed'—fished out to the point where they cannot reproduce themselves. [1]

Must read:

For a Greenpeace guide to choosing seafood in Canada, visit: www.greenpeace.ca/redlist

Where to start:

There are two key issues that determine whether or not a fishery is sustainable. The first: how healthy is the population or 'stock'? The second: what is the method used to catch or raise the fish?

Want more?

1. Find out how it was caught.

Line-caught fish are often the best option but there are some important distinctions. Long-line fishing—often used for tuna—uses long fishing lines that are laden with hundreds of hooks. These long lines are then dragged through the ocean at the back of a boat, catching non-target and threatened species like seabirds, sharks and turtles. Rod-and-line fishing, on the other hand, has just one hook on the end, and does far less damage.

Small markets or health food stores will often be able to tell you how seafood was caught. Choose line-caught fish from small-scale fisheries wherever possible. If you must eat tuna, then go for skipjack caught by rod-and-line (avoid long-line caught tuna). Unfortunately, most canned tuna is not sustainable. For shellfish, choose hand-gathered scallops, winkles, clams, oysters and mussels instead of dredged ones. Look for pot-caught crabs, langoustines (scampi) and lobsters.

2. Think carefully about farmed fish.

Aquaculture is often promoted as the solution to sustainable fisheries and has undergone a massive growth over the last fifty years. Unfortunately, with the exception of some shellfish farms and freshwater fish, most aquaculture increases the pressure on over-exploited marine ecosystems. Some problems:

⁎ Wild fish are used to feed farmed fish, wasting valuable protein. It takes over three tonnes of wild fish to produce one tonne of farmed salmon.

⁎ Industrial fishing for smaller fish like sardines and anchovies for use in fishmeal has caused massive disruption to marine food webs.

⁎ Disease spreads easily from farmed to wild populations, further depleting wild stocks.

* Water and surrounding ecosystems are polluted by chemicals, antibiotics and vaccines used to control diseases in intensively farmed fisheries.

3. **Ask questions.**

If your local grocery store or favourite restaurant is offering unsustainable fish, let them know. Visit Greenpeace's Redlist at www.greenpeace.ca/redlist. Some key questions to ask include:

* Is it endangered or over-fished?

* How and where was it caught or farmed?

* If it's farmed, is it farmed sustainably?

* Is it likely to contain a dangerous build-up of mercury and other toxins?

4. **Protest unsustainable fishing methods.**

Bottom-trawling is a fishing method that drags huge, heavy nets suspended between large metal doors along the sea floor, crushing nearly everything in its path. Evidence indicates that deep water life forms are very slow to recover from the damage. If they recover at all, it can take decades to hundreds of years. If allowed to continue, the bottom-trawlers of the high seas will destroy deep-sea species before we have even discovered what's out there in the first place (we have better maps of the moon than we do of the ocean floor). Scientists and some governments are calling for a global moratorium on high seas bottom-trawling.

For more information on fishing methods, visit: www.oceans.greenpeace.org

For Greenpeace's full Redlist, visit:
www.greenpeace.ca/redlist

Examples of better seafood options include:

Atlantic and Pacific herring - Herring are a relatively short-lived species with an early age of maturity and a fast growth rate. Fishing gear used to capture herring generally have minimal impacts on habitats and ecosystems and low rates of by-catch.

Farmed mussels - Mussels cultured in their native region using strict safety and environmental standards have a low impact on the surrounding environment. Mussels rely on natural organisms and other non-living, organic matter for food. That means that mussels raised in a natural environment don't require fish meal from wild sources. In addition, mussels remove nutrients from the water column as they feed as opposed to farmed salmon, for example, which contribute large quantities of nutrient waste to the surrounding environment.

Seafoods to avoid include:

Tuna - All stocks are largely fully exploited and many are over-fished. Southern bluefin tuna is listed as critically endangered while bigeye tuna is listed as vulnerable. The main two methods used to catch tuna—purse seine nets and long-lines—have a very high rate of by-catch of small fish, sharks, marlin, swordfish and turtles. While there are a few tuna options that are better than others, it is hard (if not impossible) for consumers to trace what's in the can back to a sustainable fishery. (Greenpeace Canada's sustainable seafood campaign is asking retailers to trace some tunas back to companies with better fishing practices. Stayed tuned at www.greenpeace.ca/redlist)

Farmed Atlantic salmon - Wild Atlantic salmon stocks are severely depleted due to overfishing. Farmed Atlantic salmon does not offer a good alternative as wild-caught fish are used to make salmon feed.

Salmon are intensively farmed—the resulting diseases spread to wild fish. In addition, chemicals, antibiotics and waste from farms pollute the environment.

Orange roughy - Orange roughy is extremely vulnerable to fishing pressure because it grows slowly, does not reproduce until thirty years of age and lives up to 130 years. Boats fishing for orange roughy use destructive, heavy trawl gear that destroys ocean habitat.

Tropical shrimp - Tropical shrimp are captured by bottom-trawling methods which take high levels of by-catch, including finfish and endangered and threatened sea turtles. Shrimp and prawns can also be raised in ponds that destroy mangrove forests and have significant negative social impacts.

Atlantic cod - Despite strict management in the US and Canada, cod populations remain over-fished. Canadian populations are so low that some are listed as endangered or threatened.

Please note:

Consumption advisories due to mercury can change over time. To read more about mercury advisories, visit: www.oceansalive.org

Note on sources: Most of the information in this section is courtesy of Greenpeace Canada and www.seachoice.org

Right: Some fishing methods generate high levels of 'by-catch.' That means that they trap and kill non-target species.

SEAFOOD

SHOPPING

OVERVIEW

Nothing is new. Everything comes to us with its own biography. Most products are trailing strands of the most urgent narratives on the planet today: neo-liberal economic globalization, colonialism, ancient forest destruction, toxic pollution, climate change. Given all the social and environmental implications of contemporary markets, it is difficult to recommend specific consumer goods—the context itself is flawed. We will not find the answers to the questions of economic injustice and environmental destruction in shopping. We will find it in political change.

At the same time, there are steps you can take with respect to your consumer habits that will make a difference. You are probably doing them already: saving, reusing, patching, fixing, retrofitting, trading, reinventing the things you already have. Here are a few ideas on how you can cut down the volume and the impact of your purchases.

Fact:

In 2006, Canadian residents spent $391.3 billion in retail stores. [1] Our annual purchases include approximately 27.1 kilograms of red meat [2], twenty-two kilograms of disposable tissue products (like toilet paper) [3] and forty-seven litres of bottled water per person. [4]

Must read:

The No-Nonsense Guide to Fair Trade. David Ransom. New Internationalist Publications: Oxford. 2001.

Where to start:

- ✲ Only buy what you will use.
- ✲ Choose items that are built to last.
- ✲ Fix items you already have.
- ✲ Choose used goods.
- ✲ Always shop with a list.
- ✲ Buy in bulk.
- ✲ Consider production and disposal.
- ✲ Read labels.
- ✲ Look for fair trade certified items.
- ✲ Develop relationships with retailers and producers.

Want more?

1. Only buy what you will use.

Think about what you need before you go to the store and always bring a list. If you won't use it, leave it in the store.

2. Choose items that will last. Fix what you already have.

Don't give up on your television set or your favourite pair of jeans—there's a good chance they can be rehabilitated. Develop relationships with tailors and repair shops in your area. Learn to sew if you don't already know how.

3. Choose used goods.

Use hand-me-downs—especially for children—and trade clothing with friends and relatives. Websites, consignment shops, used clothing stores and vintage boutiques are all great places to buy and sell a variety of items including clothing and furniture.

SHOPPING

4. Buy in bulk and bring your own shopping bags.

Start by carrying a small, collapsible cloth bag with you at all times for random purchases. If you want to go further, create a shopping kit. Choose a backpack and keep it stocked with bags and reusable, food-safe containers for bulk items. If possible, shop at stores that offer a variety of bulk items and that let you bring in containers to refill.

5. Avoid excess packaging.

If you can't find an item in bulk, look for products without excess

packaging. Look for containers that can be recycled and that contain recycled content. Contact your municipality for a list of material accepted by your local recycling program. Write to manufacturers and ask them to cut down on their packaging.

6. Read labels.

Read ingredient lists and look for specific labels and certifications. Choose certified organic, certified fair trade and Forest Stewardship Council certified products. Check to see if the product and packaging is recycled and/or recyclable.

7. Consider production and disposal.

Once you've decided to buy something, ask yourself some basic questions. How was it produced? Under what conditions? Where did the raw materials come from? Is there a more environmental option? And, when I'm done with it, how will I dispose of it? Are there facilities to recycle this item where I live? Is there someone who can use it when I'm done? If your purchase will end up as landfill, you might want to reconsider.

8. Beware of the sell.

There are no rules governing words like 'natural' and 'ethical.' On top of that, savvy advertisers often co-opt progressive ideas and images to sell products. Look for recognized certifications and ask questions.

9. Choose fair trade.

In principle, fair trade means that everyone involved in the process of production is properly compensated for their work. In addition, fair trade should be socially and environmentally sustainable. Fair trade is not charity, it is justice. When consumers buy products at artificially low prices at the expense of workers and small producers, we are, if inadvertently, stealing.

Look for fair trade certified products. Common fair trade certified food items available in Canada include coffee, tea, chocolate, bananas, coffee and

sugar. Sustainably produced furniture, clothing and gift items are available as well.

For a list of fair trade products and retailers in Canada, visit: www.transfair.ca

The global network of Fair Trade Organizations (IFAT) certifies suppliers (as opposed to products) in Canada and around the world.

For a list of IFAT certified suppliers in Canada, visit: www.ifat.org

If a product is not certified, it still might conform to fair trade principles, but you will have to ask questions and establish this for yourself. Ask where and how the product was made and under what conditions. If your local store doesn't stock fair trade items, demand that they do.

10. Find responsible and environmental retailers.

You are probably already attached to a few stores, websites or products that reflect your interest in the environment and social justice. There are many small businesses (including web-based ones) and co-op grocery stores across Canada that go out of their way to operate sustainably. Find that local cafe that offers fair trade coffee and the co-op that sells groceries and cleaning products in bulk and be fiercely loyal.

11. **Develop a relationship with your store. Develop a relationship with your products.**

.We're not talking about the kind of emotional attachment advertisers try to inspire between, say, you and your brand of deodorant. We're talking about getting to know the people and processes responsible for taking raw materials and delivering them to you in the form of finished products.

If you have a long-term relationship with a business and the people who work there, you will have greater access to information about the products you buy. You'll have more influence, too. Whether you're shopping at a big-box chain or a corner store, ask for what you want. Sometimes, you might have to send a letter or an email to head office to get results. Take it one step at a time and remember: stores respond to consumer pressure.

12. **Support small businesses.**

Small business owners often work and/or live in the neighbourhoods they serve. They can also be more flexible and responsive to customer requests and preferences. If you have the opportunity, buy directly from the producer. Visit farmers' markets and buy from local artists and designers.

Right: Support environmentally friendly small businesses including co-ops and farmers' markets.

greenpeace
living

SHOPPING

SPECIAL EVENTS

OVERVIEW

Religious holidays, weddings, graduations and other special events are an opportunity to spread joy. And to generate pollution. Pesticide-laden flowers, disposable wrapping and plastic cutlery can give happy occasions a sinister second significance. Use special events as a way to explore the growing array of sustainable, fair trade or recycled options available for everything from roses to chocolate to wedding rings.

Where to start:

❋ Choose a local, organic menu.

❋ Choose fair trade flowers, chocolate, coffee and tea.

❋ Consider making a donation to your favourite charity as a gift.

❋ Try constructing a waste-free event.

Want more?

1. Choose an organic, local menu.

To cut down on both agricultural chemicals and greenhouse gas emissions, opt for as many local, certified organic ingredients as you can fit into your meal. Try and construct a '100-mile menu'— a meal assembled from ingredients found within a 100-mile radius of your home. But don't stop at food. Consider locally grown, organic flowers (make sure to ask about labour conditions if they're not fair trade certified) and local organic wine.

2. Choose fair trade food, flowers and gifts.

While it's important to choose organic and local, it's also crucial to consider the labour conditions under which a specific item was produced. Fair trade certified products in Canada include roses, chocolate, coffee and tea. For more information on fair trade items available in Canada, visit www.transfair.ca. Consider incorporating fair trade certified coffee, tea and chocolate into your meal and decorating with fair trade flowers.

While it can be difficult to find fair trade certified gift items, some retailers have established their own, ethical relationships with producers. In general, look for items that are union-made, marketed directly by artisans or produced by workers' co-ops and/or community initiatives. You can also buy directly from artisans or workers' co-ops and other sustainable producers online. Research a few key sources for gift items and stick with them. Wherever you are shopping, ask questions and always take the opportunity to demand products that are sustainably produced.

3. Choose recycled and rented.

Okay, it's your special day and it's up to you. But you might want to consider sourcing vintage outfits, borrowing a fabulous dress you admired on a friend or simply renting and returning your duds. You also can collaborate with a tailor to rework an existing garment into the wedding gear of your dreams. Consider choosing used wedding rings or rings made from recycled materials.

4. Choose reusable.

Why shouldn't you and your guests enjoy the day long after it's gone? There are countless items that can be salvaged from your special event. Consider using potted plants instead of flowers and designing practical centre-pieces that guests can take home. Try choosing outfits for you and your wedding party that can be worn again—in everyday life. Do a quick inventory of your special event—if an item can't be returned, reused, composted or recycled, consider doing without it.

5. Avoid disposables.

Stay away from disposable plastic and styrofoam. Consider renting or borrowing cups, plates and cutlery. You can also find biodegradable, compostable tableware. When giving gifts, use reusable gift bags for wrapping.

6. Invite responsibly.

If you're going to send paper invitations to your special event, make sure they're printed on 100 percent post-consumer, processed chlorine-free paper. Great ancient forest friendly paper is available in Canada in a number of weights, colours and textures. And remember to ask your printer for vegetable-based inks. For more information on ancient forest friendly paper, visit: www.ancientforestfriendly.com

A better option: avoid paper completely and send out a beautifully designed email invitation. You'll save money, paper and greenhouse gas emissions at the same time.

7. Give green.

As mentioned, if you're going to choose a gift from the world of the material, make sure to calculate its environmental and social consequences. Making it yourself is often the best way to make sure the process is eco-friendly. The best choice for the environment: make a donation to your favourite not-for-profit.

You can also give the gift of experience: dance classes, language lessons or the promise of a special, home-cooked meal. Or services: offer to design a website, take wedding photos or help plant a garden.

Consider a fabulous 'present for the planet' courtesy of Greenpeace. Visit www.presentsfortheplanet.ca for a bursting catalogue of waste-free virtual gifts.

TISSUE PRODUCTS

OVERVIEW

Toilet paper, napkins, paper towels and facial tissue are probably the most disposable products in our lives. We use them once and then throw them away. On top of that, tissue products are often made with virgin tree fibre from ancient forests like Canada's Boreal Forest. Right now, forests that have been around for more than 10,000 years are being flushed down toilets across the country. Fortunately, recycled tissue products are widely available. Frequently used products like toilet paper are a good place to start changing your buying habits right away.

Must read:

For information on forest friendly tissue products, visit: http://tissue.greenpeace.ca

Greenpeace is asking companies to stop using pulp from ancient forests to make disposable tissue products. For information and activist resources, visit: www.greenpeace.ca

Fact:

In Canada, over 700,000 tonnes of disposable tissue products are used each year. The average Canadian uses about twenty-two kilograms of disposable tissue products each year, including a hundred rolls of toilet paper. If each household in Canada replaced one roll of virgin toilet paper with just one roll of recycled toilet paper, we could save 47,962 trees, 3,204 cubic metres of landfill space and 65.5 million litres of water. [1]

Where to start:

Buy only 100 percent post-consumer recycled toilet paper and tissue products from now on.

Want more?

1. Reduce or eliminate your use of paper towels, facial tissue and napkins.

In our disposable consumer society, paper products like towels and napkins are the most disposable products of all. Up until recently, cloth towels and napkins were the norm. Then giant paper companies stepped in and helped to create a 'need' for disposable tissue products. Reclaim the old days and reduce your tissue product consumption by re-embracing washables.

2. Choose recycled tissue products.

Tissue products, including toilet paper made from post-consumer recycled fibre, are the best bet. The higher the post-consumer content, the better. If you can't find products containing post-consumer recycled fibre, then just plain recycled is the next best thing. There are a variety of brands with high recycled content available across Canada. Many grocery stores also have

in-store brands that are 100 percent recycled.

3. Pre-consumer recycled vs. post-consumer recycled.

Pre-consumer recycled material (sometimes called simply 'recycled material or paper') in tissue products or paper comes from the bits and pieces left over during the manufacturing process. In other words, pre-consumer recycled material has never been used by consumers— it comes straight from wasteful processes in a paper mill or factory. Post-consumer recycled material comes from sources like old newspapers or office paper collected by blue box systems across the country—it has been used by consumers and then recycled. Whenever possible, use the product with the highest possible post-consumer content. When you buy post-consumer, you are literally re-using fibre from another product, rewarding businesses that use efficient processes and supporting local recycling programs.

(Please note: post-consumer paper is almost never totally chlorine-free, since the original paper may have contained chlorine. Look for post-consumer products that are processed chlorine-free— manufactured without chlorine bleach. This book, for example, is printed on paper that is 100 percent post-consumer recycled, 100 percent processed chlorine-free.)

4. Careful with those tricky recycling symbols.

Recycling symbols in the packaging of disposable tissue products can be confusing. Sometimes the recycled symbol refers only to the plastic packaging or the cardboard box— not the tissue product itself. Other times, the recycled symbol refers to the cardboard roll in the center of the toilet paper or paper towels. Read the fine print to make sure you're getting a recycled product. And remember—recycled and recyclable are not the same thing. Ideally, you're looking for a recycled tissue product with recyclable packaging.

5. Stay away from chlorine and other toxics.

To make paper look white, manufacturers use bleaching processes that often include chlorine. Look for products labeled totally chlorine-free (TCF) or processed chlorine-free (PCF).

6. Ask for what you want.

Tell the manager at your local store that you want to buy post-consumer recycled, processed chlorine-free tissue products. If you don't see recycled options, ask for them.

7. Avoid these companies.

At press time, Kimberly-Clark (Kleenex, Cottonelle), Kruger (Spongetowels, Cashmere, Scotties, Purex—regular version, not Enviroplus brands), Procter & Gamble (Charmin, Puffs, Bounty) and Irving Paper (Royale, Majesta) had particularly bad environmental records, contributing to ancient forest destruction—some manufacturing some tissue products with no recycled fibre at all.

For more information on these companies and their brands of tissue products visit: http://tissue.greenpeace.ca and www.kleercut.net

TOILETRIES

OVERVIEW

When you buy face cream, toothpaste, shampoo, hair dyes, cosmetics and other personal care products, you are entering a Wild West of government regulation. When Canada's current overarching chemical legislation was introduced in 1988, 23,000 chemicals were grandfathered in. That means that older chemicals haven't been subjected to the scrutiny applied to newer formulations. Although the federal government has earmarked 4,000 of these older chemicals for safety assessments, the current chemical landscape is still pretty much wide open. [1] Anything goes—carcinogens, mutagens, reproductive toxins, endocrine disruptors. It's all part of the average Canadian's beauty routine. [2]

And—toxic as they are in their own way—it's time to turn our backs on common media representations of 'youth' and 'beauty.' Forget what you see on television. Forget it right now. Television parades an endless cast of gender, class and cultural stereotypes through our living rooms each night to sell us things we don't need. It's insulting. Part of changing the world is learning to outrun the mythological women and men invented by corporations to keep the status quo firmly in place and sell us a lifetime's worth of face cream and diet pills. Look around you on the bus. Everyone is beautiful.

Fact:

You are already beautiful.

Where to start:

✽ Love your face.

✽ Use fewer products.

✽ Look for products that are certified organic.

✽ Avoid synthetic fragrances.

✽ Choose packaging that is refillable, made of recycled material and recyclable.

✽ Ask manufacturers and retailers as many questions as you can.

✽ Remember that it is okay to have hips, it is okay to have pores, it is okay to age.

Please note: This is not a health guide. We have listed the substances and practices that are particularly harmful to the environment. Many chemicals used in toiletries have been linked to cancer and other health risks. This is not a comprehensive manual for choosing healthy cosmetics or toiletries.

Want more?

1. **Use fewer products.**

Ask yourself how many different types of shower gels, eye shadows, toners and moisturizers you actually need. Only buy what you will use and only use the basics. And, as Tanya Ha points out in her fantastic green guide, *Greeniology*, the best way to look great is to take care of yourself: eat right, drink water, exercise and sleep. [3]

2. **Choose products that are unscented or scented with natural substances.**

Artificial musks (also referred to as synthetic scent) are fragrances added to personal care and household products like shower gels, soaps, hand lotions and perfumes. They are persistent, bioaccumulative chemicals (they accumulate in the tissue of living things) and some have been linked with hormone disruption in humans. [4] Look out for words like 'fragrance,' 'masking agent,' 'parfum' and 'artificial musk' on product ingredients and avoid them.

Keep in mind, a product labelled 'unscented' can contain a certain percentage of scent—usually to mask the odours of other ingredients. 5 To find out if a product is actually free of synthetic scent, contact the manufacturer.

3. **Avoid phthalates and other toxic chemicals.**

Phthalates represent one group of chemical compounds you should do your best to avoid. They are used for a variety of purposes including to soften plastic, to

increase the staying power of fragrances and to keep nail polish from chipping. Many phthalates are known to be reproductive and developmental toxins. 6 They are commonly found in cosmetic and personal care products including nail polish, perfumes and deodorizers.

To avoid phthalates and other toxic chemicals like parabens (which are suspected to have links to breast cancer), start reading ingredient lists. It's not always easy to tell what's what— and phthalates aren't usually listed as ingredients—so it may be easiest to research a couple of brands available in your neighbourhood and then stick to what you know.

4. **Choose certified organic products.**

Advertisers toss words like 'natural,' 'botanical' and even 'organic' around pretty easily. Look for products that are 100 percent certified organic or at least contain a high percentage of certified organic ingredients. A product can have some organic content and still contain harmful chemicals.

5. Choose certified organic and/or reusable menstrual products.

We can't make health recommendations here, but we can tell you that the less waste, the better. And, of course, organic is always a good bet. Some women choose reusable, washable cotton pads. Other options for cutting down on waste include tampons without applicators and specially made, reusable menstrual cups. Organic cotton, non-chlorine bleached tampons and pads are also available.

6. Think about packaging.

Some companies and retailers will let you bring packaging (or your own containers) back to the store to refill. Others run inhouse recycling programs for, say, empty lipstick tubes. Look for packaging that is minimal, post-consumer recycled and recyclable. And, as with all products, avoid PVC (#3), polycarbonate (#7) and polystyrene (#6) plastic packaging.
(See 'Plastics and non-stick coatings')

7. Ask for what you want.

Tell the manager at your local store that you want to buy products that are toxic-free and responsibly packaged.

8. Research.

Since ingredient lists can be confusing, incomplete or subject to change, your best bet is to source a few brands and retailers. Ask as many questions as you can until you find a few key naturally scented or scent-free products that are free of toxic chemicals.

For an online database of products rated for safety by the Environmental Working Group, visit: www.ewg.org/reports/skindeep

You can also visit *The Guide to Less Toxic Products* at www.lesstoxicguide.ca

TRANSPORTATION

OVERVIEW

Transportation is an area in which individuals can make a significant difference to Canada's greenhouse gas emissions and quality of life. In Canada, road transportation accounts for roughly half the average person's annual 5.7 tonnes of greenhouse emissions and plays a large part in Canada's total contribution to global climate change.

Driving also contributes to smog, particularly in urban areas, with real consequences for health and productivity. According to the Ontario Medical Association, air pollution contributed to about 5,800 premature deaths in 2005 in Ontario alone and cost the province close to a billion dollars. [1]

Airline travel is also shockingly destructive, costing the climate literally tonnes of greenhouse gas emissions each time you take a flight.

Fact:

Cars and trucks generate approximately 12 percent of Canada's greenhouse gas emissions. [2]

Must read:

Natural Resources Canada's Office of Energy Efficiency has compiled valuable information on transportation and climate change, fuel-efficient vehicles and green driving at: www.oee.nrcan.gc.ca

The Climate Action Network—a coalition of environmental organizations including Greenpeace—also has excellent resources for personal and political action. Visit: www.climateactionnetwork.ca

Simple step:

If you are currently driving to work, resolve to bike, walk or take public transportation once a week. Once you find the best way and the best route, make it a habit.

Where to start:

✱ Take public transportation, walk or ride a bike.

✱ If you have to drive, carpool.

✱ Choose the most fuel-efficient vehicle you can find.

✱ Don't idle.

✱ Follow the speed limit—it will cut down on your fuel consumption.

✱ Don't use the air conditioner. Roll down the windows instead.

✱ Advocate for bike-friendly cities.

✱ Avoid airplane travel. Choose the train and bus for short trips.

✱ Advocate for well-funded public transportation in your municipality.

Want more?

1. Don't drive.

Driving is unsustainable—period. The culture of driving chews up land for roads and parking, spews greenhouse gas emissions into the air (about 86 million tonnes per year in Canada) [3], contributes to smog and generally takes up too much environmental room. Find alternatives to driving. Take public transportation. Many municipalities offer a monthly transit pass. Get one, keep it with you at all times and hop on and off the subway, bus or streetcar whenever you want. Biking is also an excellent option (just wear a helmet). You can also take a taxi and, of course, walk.

2. If you have to drive, reduce your impact.

If you are going to drive, here are a few ways to make less of a dent in the environment:

✱ Don't drive a Sports Utility Vehicle (SUV). SUVs are about one third less fuel-efficient and produce up to 75 percent more emissions than other passenger vehicles. 4

✳ Carpool. The fewer individual cars on the road, the better. On top of saving greenhouse gas emissions, you'll extend the life of your car and save money on fuel and parking. You'll also drive less, spend more time looking out the window and get to know your co-workers and neighbours better.

To calculate how much money and carbon you could save by carpooling, visit: www.carpool.ca

✳ Share a car. Seriously. Share it with family members, friends and even neighbours. Another option is to join a car sharing service—some will allow you to rent cars for a reasonable price by the hour. If you don't like the idea of sharing, consider giving up your car and renting for a few days at a time.

✳ Choose fuel-efficient cars.

National Resources Canada has ratings and resources for choosing fuel-efficient vehicles at: www.oee.nrcan.gc.ca

✳ Don't idle. If you are stopped for an extended period of time, turn off the car. Letting an engine idle for just ten minutes a day can create a quarter of a tonne of carbon emissions each year.

To start your own 'stop idling' campaign, check out valuable resources at: www.oee.nrcan.gc.ca

✳ Follow the speed limit. The faster you drive, the more fuel you use. Driving at 120 kilometres an hour instead of 100 kilometres an hour can increase your fuel consumption by 20 percent. 5

✳ Keep your vehicle in good condition—have it checked regularly. Make sure the anti-pollution system is working well. Pay attention to your tire pressure—soft tires increase fuel consumption.

✳ Turn off the air conditioning. Roll down the windows instead. You'll save up to 20 percent on fuel costs. 6

3. Reduce airplane travel.

It's shocking but true—if you are a frequent flyer, eliminating or reducing airplane travel may be one of the most important things you can do for the environment. Airplane travel is one of the planet's fastest growing sources of greenhouse gas emissions. It has also by far the greatest climate impact of any mode of transportation. According to a report by the Climate Action Network Europe and the European Federation for Transport and the Environment, air travel is between two to ten times more climate-intensive than surface transport and accounts for somewhere between 4 to 9 percent of human-generated climate impacts (this includes the combined effects of a number of factors including carbon dioxide, nitrous oxide and contrails). [7] Avoid planes for short-haul trips—take the train. Depending on the criteria you are using to calculate emissions, a return flight from Toronto to Vancouver can generate somewhere between one and two tonnes of greenhouse gas emissions per person. [8] Each Canadian produces approximately 5.7 tonnes of individual greenhouse gas emissions per year. If you are flying a lot, chances are you're clocking well above the Canadian average.

4. Advocate for public transportation.

Maybe you're still driving because efficient public transportation isn't available in your neighbourhood. If so, ask for it. Contact your municipal representatives and your transit authority and tell them what you want. Remind federal and provincial governments that Canadians expect them to provide comprehensive funding for public transit.

Green business tip:

Organize a carpool. Better yet, if your workplace is accessible by transit and you're not carrying heavy equipment back and forth, lobby your employer to provide or subsidize monthly transit passes. Some municipal transportation systems will offer bulk discount rates for workplaces and schools.

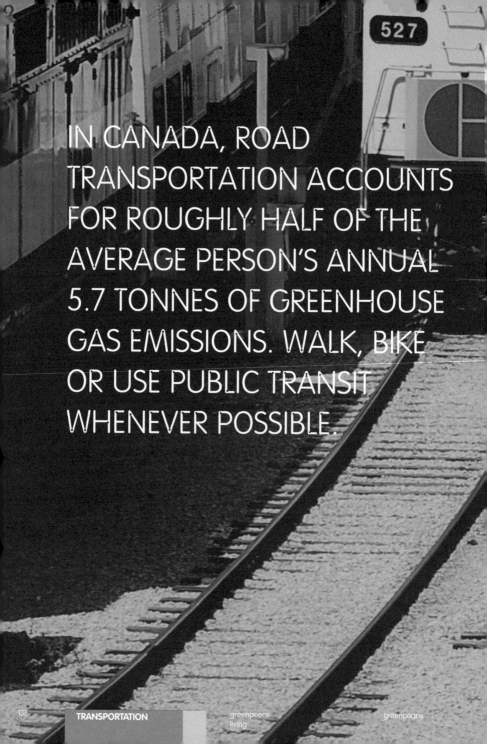

IN CANADA, ROAD TRANSPORTATION ACCOUNTS FOR ROUGHLY HALF OF THE AVERAGE PERSON'S ANNUAL 5.7 TONNES OF GREENHOUSE GAS EMISSIONS. WALK, BIKE OR USE PUBLIC TRANSIT WHENEVER POSSIBLE.

greenpeace
living

greenpeace

TRANSPORTATION

WASTE

OVERVIEW

If you took all the non-hazardous solid waste generated from all sectors in Canada in 2002 and gave every resident an equal share, we would each end up with about 971 kilograms of garbage on our doorsteps (or, to help you visualize, about thirteen adult men of about average Canadian weight). If you made each Canadian keep the waste he or she was personally responsible for generating, we would each end up with approximately 383 kilograms of garbage haunting our dreams (or about five men).

Some estimates have Canada as one of the biggest waste-generators in the world—ranking second behind the United States. Lucky for us, household waste accounts for a full 40 percent of Canada's solid waste (although this statistic doesn't include any mess Canadian industry might be making in other countries). In other words—there's a lot individual consumers can do to shrink Canada's landfills, empty out our incinerators and generally stop the madness. 1

Fact:

In 2002, Canadian households generated twelve million tonnes of waste.

Where to start:

* Look for ways to eliminate waste before it happens. Buy in bulk, buy used and avoid over-packaged products.

* Consider reusable as opposed to disposable products.

* Spend an afternoon getting to know your local recycling program.

* Create a user-friendly, easy recycling system for your home and workplace.

* If your community doesn't have 'green bin' pick-up (or even if they do), consider starting your own compost.

* Make sure to properly dispose of hazardous waste.

* Familiarize yourself with waste-related issues in your community.

Want more?

1. **Eliminate waste before it happens.**

In 2002, only one-fifth of Canada's non-hazardous waste was diverted from disposal by recycling and composting programs. That means that approximately 80 percent of our waste is destined for landfill or incineration. The best solution for waste: don't create it at all. Choose reusable products—like batteries and razors—over disposable ones. Avoid over-packaged products and buy in bulk whenever possible. Take other, simple steps to eliminate waste: bring a cloth bag shopping, carry a reusable mug and, if you can, consider cutting out bottled water.

2. **Get to know your local recycling program.**

Most local recycling programs will take #1 plastics, #2 plastics and a range of paper products. Some programs go much further, accepting a range of organic waste from food scraps to facial tissue. Take an afternoon and get to know your local recycling program— go through your municipality's website or give them a call. Find out what's in and what's out, including details on hazardous waste disposal and make sure to get a schedule. Then post a list and a schedule on the fridge for future reference.

There might be additional options for recycling in your area. For example, some manufacturers will take back cell phones and computers at the end of their lifecycles. In addition, some not-for-profits and government programs will accept gently used computers, ink cartridges, software and even computer accessories.

3. **Set up a user-friendly recycling system.**

Make it easy on yourself. Once you find out what to recycle—and when—set up a neat, simple recycling system. Try setting up two or three small garbage cans (under the kitchen counter if they'll fit) and designating them for specific recycling categories.

Some people like to keep a small plastic container with a tight lid (often available at hardware stores or through municipalities) on the counter for food scraps. However you decide to do it, make sure your system is easy and accessible.

4. Compost.

Compost is great for the garden and a real way to cut down on your personal contribution to Canada's landfills. In addition to causing needless waste, organic materials that end up in landfills generate methane—a powerful greenhouse gas—as they decompose. In fact, according to Environment Canada, landfills are responsible for a full 38 percent of Canada's methane emissions. [2]

You can create compost yourself or, if it's available, use a municipal composting program. A composter will take most of your organic waste including kitchen scraps and yard waste and turn them into a rich humus for your lawn or garden. Some items that shouldn't be composted include meat, dairy, fish, oil, fat and pet waste. If composting directly through a municipal curbside program, get a list of do's and don'ts from them.

Many municipalities offer discounts on composters and composting tips. You can also buy a composter at a hardware store or try to make your own.

For composting tips from Environment Canada, visit: www.ns.ec.gc.ca

For detailed information on composting methods, visit the Composting Council of Canada at: www.compost.org

5. Properly dispose of hazardous substances.

Hazardous waste includes anything corrosive, toxic, flammable, explosive or poisonous. Hazardous waste should not be put out for regular garbage pick up or poured down drains or sewers. Some examples of hazardous waste include:

* Compact fluorescent light bulbs (they contain small amounts of mercury).

* Toxic cleaning products including any products labelled poisonous, explosive, corrosive or flammable.

* Batteries including car batteries and spent rechargeables.

* Toxic paints, varnishes, sealants and coatings.

* Motor oil and propane tanks.

* Electronics including televisions, computers, cellphones and VCRs.

* Pesticides and herbicides.

* Syringes.

Contact your municipality to find out about its hazardous waste programs. Many municipalities have special drop-off depots or 'toxic taxi' services for hazardous waste. For more details on how to deal with used electronics, please see the 'Electronics' section. Keep all hazardous waste safely out of reach of children.

Green business tip:

Canada Waste Reduction week . has produced a kit for waste reduction in work places. The kit includes waste assessment forms and industry-specific tips: www.wrwcanada.com

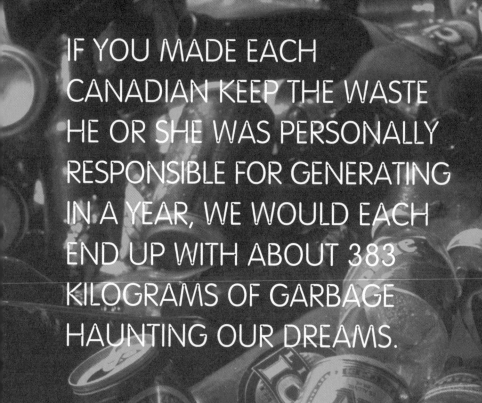

IF YOU MADE EACH CANADIAN KEEP THE WASTE HE OR SHE WAS PERSONALLY RESPONSIBLE FOR GENERATING IN A YEAR, WE WOULD EACH END UP WITH ABOUT 383 KILOGRAMS OF GARBAGE HAUNTING OUR DREAMS.

greenpeace
living

greenpeace

WATER

OVERVIEW

For the most part, we have been working with the same water supply for billions of years. We have some on the surface, some in the ground and some in the atmosphere—each source swapping places with the other as part of a miraculous cycle. But humans have started to interrupt this cycle: polluting water sources with toxic chemicals; pumping dizzying amounts of water out of underground aquifers to irrigate industrial agricultural projects and supply bottled water conglomerates; paving over the soft ground that filters rain water back into rivers and lakes; melting glaciers with our greenhouse gas emissions. Available fresh water—water we can use for drinking and irrigation—makes up less than one half of one percent of the world's water supply. And we are using it fast—mostly to supply industrial agricultural projects.

While the domestic realm represents only a fraction of global water use, there are a variety of measures you can take to reduce your personal water use and keep water in public hands. Canadians, in particular, have a lot of room for improvement—the average Canadian household uses 500,000 litres of water per year. [1] A bonus to limiting your water use—you can map your progress on your water bill. Check your water bills as you move through these tips and watch them steadily reduce.

Fact:

According to *Blue Gold*, the three biggest corporations delivering privatized water services around the world—Suez-ONDEO, Vivendi-Veolia and RWE-Thames—are growing at a rate of 10 percent each year. Between 2002 and 2006, the bottled water industry—another form of privatized water delivery dominated by Nestlé, Coca-Cola and PepsiCo.—increased its global revenues from US$22 billion to US$100 billion. [2] Right now, approximately 2.6 billion people lack access to basic sanitation and more than 1 billion people live without access to clean water. [3]

Must read:

For information on water in Canada, visit: www.canadians.org and www.eausecours.org

Blue Gold by Maude Barlow and Tony Clarke. Stoddart Publishing. 2002.

Water Inc. by Varda Burstyn. Verso: London. 2005.

Where to start:

✻ Reconsider bottled water.

✻ Eat less meat.

✻ Use a dual-flush toilet.

✻ Install water-efficient shower heads and faucets.

✻ Choose water-efficient appliances.

✻ Get help to disconnect your downspout.

✻ Replace grass and pavement with native plants and bushes.

✻ Fix leaks right away.

WATER

Want more?

1. Resist water privatization.

Clean water is a human right, a life-giving force that should be universally available and commonly owned. Right now, private corporations are increasing their collective grip on the planet's dwindling water supply, treating water as a commodity like any other—vulnerable to market forces and the 'laws' of supply and demand. A small handful of large corporations offer the private administration of water services around the world—anything from replacing aging pipes to providing waste treatment services and water delivery.

Privatization is exacerbated by global trade and monetary regimes, which often demand that countries receiving loans or loan guarantees undertake the privatization of public services, including water. To make matters worse, basic, low-technology water conservation measures are not highly profitable and are not generally practiced where water is extracted or managed for profit.

In 2008, the United Nations Human Rights Council met to discuss a proposed resolution to recognize water and sanitation as human rights. The resolution, which was put forward by Germany and Spain, did not pass, largely due to Canada's vigorous efforts to derail the process. [4] "Recognizing water as a human right is vital to ensuring that governments address the reality of more than a billion people who are currently without access to clean water," said Council of Canadians chairperson Maude Barlow in reaction. "It is shocking that Canada would work with the United States to oppose this fundamental right." [5]

For information on how to protest water privatization visit Navdanya's website at: www.navdanya.org or the Council of Canadians website at: www.canadians.org

2. Reconsider bottled water.

Another stream of privatization is the bottled water industry, which pumps billions of litres of water—water that belongs to everyone—

out of underground aquifers each year and sells it back to us for profit. In addition to charging money for a public resource, bottled water companies are also responsible for hundreds of millions of virgin plastic bottles. According to the Earth Policy Institute, manufacturers use 1.5 million barrels of oil each year to produce bottles for the US bottled water market alone. [6]

Unfortunately, water in some Canadian jurisdictions is still not safe to drink and residents suffer from continual boiled water advisories. Deregulation at the provincial level and genuine negligence by the federal government have contributed to boiled water advisories and water safety scares in jurisdictions across Canada and in First Nations communities in particular. If you are lucky enough to live in a community where water is considered safe to drink, rethink bottled water and push for strong, more effective public regulation and administration of water in all jurisdictions.

It should be noted that the use of chlorine to treat water is also a long-term concern. For personal use—and, again, in jurisdictions that are not suffering from boiled water advisories—you might want to consider using a well-maintained home filtering system.

For more information on ecological water purification, please visit: www.oceanarks.org

3. Eat less meat.

Animal products—in particular grain-fed beef—require significantly more water input than cereals like wheat, corn, barley and oats. The Worldwatch Institute estimates that it takes more than 600 gallons (2,271 litres) of water to produce meat for an average quarter pound hamburger. [7] And that's not all. Meat production is also responsible for dangerous levels of water pollution. Large factory farms store waste in 'lagoons' that can rupture and make their way into water supplies. In addition to phosphorous and nitrate pollution, waste from factory farms can also contain drug-resistant bacteria as a result of the widespread use of antibiotics. If you do eat meat, try to choose organic options whenever possible.

4. Replace toilets, showerheads and appliances.

Replace toilets, showerheads and washers with high-efficiency models. Toilets account for almost one-third of domestic water consumption. Toilets installed prior to 1980 could use up to twenty litres per flush. Today, standard 'low flush' toilets are about six litres per flush. The best toilets are 'dual flush,' which have two options—one for liquid (three litres per flush) and one for solid waste (six litres per flush). 8

Low-flow showerheads and water-efficient washing machines are readily available and can make a difference to overall household water use. (You can also find showerheads that will filter out chlorine and other contaminants.) Some municipalities have rebates available for water-efficient toilets and appliances.

If you are renting your home or aren't in a position to replace your toilet, try suspending a plastic container filled with water inside your toilet tank. The volume of the bottle will correspond to the amount of water you'll save on every flush. Make sure to install this carefully so it doesn't interfere with the operation of the toilet.

5. Don't use the toilet or sink as a garbage can.

In particular, don't throw old medications down the toilet or in the sink. They should be treated as hazardous waste. Contact your municipality to find out how to dispose of them. In the long term, government regulations should require retailers and manufacturers to take back old medications.

6. Save gray water.

If you own your home, you might want to consider installing a system that will recycle 'gray' water from the bathroom tap and shower so you can use it to water the non-edible plants in your garden. You will need help with this—consult a professional and/or your municipality.

7. Install aerators.

Aerators are small screens that go onto your taps and help to decrease water consumption by increasing the amount of air in the spray.

8. Fix leaks and running toilets.

According to the City of Toronto, a leaky toilet can waste close to 300,000 litres of water per year. 9 If you can, replace leaky toilets with high-efficiency, dual-flush models. Leaking taps can also waste astonishing amounts of water over time—fix leaks as soon as they start. One way to find out if you have a leak is to record your water meter level and then refrain from using water for a few hours. When you check the meter again, if the level has gone down, you have leaks. Another way to find out is to put some coloured food dye in the tank of your toilet. If the food dye seeps into the toilet bowl, you have a leak.

Leaks also happen at the level of municipal infrastructure and can be responsible for massive losses of water. At election time, make it clear to candidates that repair and maintenance of the municipal water system is a priority.

9. Turn off the tap.

When you're not using it, turn it off. Use a glass to brush your teeth and turn the shower off while you lather or shave (some new showerheads have a button so you can cut the water for a few seconds).

10. Only wash full loads.

Only wash full loads of dishes or clothing.

WATER

11. Take showers instead of baths.

Reasonably short showers use considerably less water than baths.

12. Water your garden in the early morning or at night.

If you water your garden in the early morning or at night, water won't evaporate as quickly.

Applying mulches to your lawn and garden will also help them to retain moisture.

13. Always choose native plants and bushes over paving and grass for your lawn.

Natural groundcover absorbs water, while rainwater that lands on hard surfaces like pavement can drag toxics into lakes and rivers and overwhelm sewer systems during storms. Native plants and grasses are more resilient to dryer weather than golf-green grass.

14. Consider disconnecting your downspout.

Some municipalities will help you disconnect the downspout that is connected to your eaves troughs. Disconnecting downspouts can help reduce sewer overflow by diverting water out of the sewer systems during heavy rainfall. Get advice when disconnecting your downspout and make sure the water is draining away from your foundation.

15. Get help from your municipality.

Many municipalities offer financial help for water-saving appliances and advice about saving water. The City of Toronto, for example, offers an 'indoor water efficiency retrofit kit.' Call your municipality for help with retrofitting, lawn care, downspout disconnection and water conservation.

Right: If you water your garden in the early morning or at night, water won't evaporate as quickly.

WOOD

OVERVIEW

Only 20 percent of the planet's ancient forests remain. [1] Two of the largest and most ecologically important are in Canada: the Boreal Forest, which stretches across the northern part of the country and the Great Bear Rainforest on the coast of British Columbia. In fact, Canada is home to more than 23 percent of the planet's remaining intact forest landscapes—more than any other country on the planet. [2]

Unfortunately, ancient forests in Canada and around the world continue to be logged for everything from disposable tissue products to furniture. The good news: concerned shoppers have a variety of options to reduce their impacts and support sustainable logging practices. Excellent, credible certification systems exist for both newly logged and reclaimed wood.

Fact:

An area of ancient forest the size of a soccer field disappears every two seconds. [3]

Must read:

The Forest Stewardship Council website lists sustainably harvested wood. Visit: www.fsccanada.org

Where to start:

✳ Choose wood certified by the Forest Stewardship Council or the Rainforest Alliance's SmartWood program (look for 'Rediscovered Wood').

✳ Choose wood from small, community-based eco-forestry programs. Look for First Nations and other locally based operations.

✳ Avoid wood treated with chemical finishings.

✳ Take action for ancient forests at www.greenpeace.ca

Want more?

1. Choose sustainably harvested, salvaged or recycled wood.

The answer for wood consumers is pretty simple. Choose reclaimed and/or Forest Stewardship Council (FSC) certified wood. You can also consider wood from small, community-based eco-forestry programs. (Note that most of the wood available in big box hardware stores is not from these types of operations.)

The FSC certifies logging operations that are managed in a socially and environmentally sound fashion. It is the only certification system in the world broadly recognized by non-governmental organizations like Greenpeace and it is the leading certification system of choice for progressive businesses. FSC certified wood and pulp is available for a number of purposes including flooring, building, furniture, paper and pencils.

For more information and a list of distributors, visit: www.fsccanada.org

While FSC certification generally applies to newly logged wood, the Rainforest Alliance's SmartWood program has developed a label for reclaimed wood (which can come from old buildings, found logs, dead trees and post-consumer sources) called 'Rediscovered Wood.' This certification system monitors the process used to recover, recycle and reuse wood according to social and environmental criteria including cultural considerations, the handling of chemicals and worker safety.

For more information on the 'Rediscovered Wood' label, visit: www.rainforest-alliance.org

Community-based eco-forestry projects can also be good options for wood purchases. Look for First Nations and other locally based operations.

2. Avoid chemical treatments.

According to the federal government's Environmental Choice Program in Canada, surface coatings like stains and varnishes release thousands of tonnes of volatile organic compounds (VOCs) into the atmosphere each year. Be careful—even certified woods can later be treated with toxics. Look for wood treated with non-toxic coatings like linseed oil, beeswax and natural resins whenever possible and get expert help before treating wood yourself.

Some coatings are also endorsed by Environment Canada's Environmental Choice program. Visit: www.environmentalchoice.com to search by product. Take a moment to read the criteria for each product.

See also, 'Paints, finishes and adhesives.'

3. Avoid unsustainably harvested and toxic wood.

You can't always tell by the type of wood you're looking at whether or not it's 'good wood.' Some tropical timber is sustainably harvested, some comes from destructive illegal logging. Some wood from Canada's forests is fair game, other wood is the result of devastating clearcutting. Fortunately, avoiding unsustainably harvested wood is easy: choose FSC certified wood or look for Rediscovered Wood certification from the Rainforest Alliance.

Chromated Copper Arsenate (CCA) treated lumber has typically been used on outdoor structures like decks, playgrounds, fencing and picnic tables. CCA can leach arsenic, chromium and copper over time, posing a potential health hazard, particularly for children. In 2003, manufacturers in Canada and the US voluntarily agreed to stop producing CCA treated wood for residential use. Suppliers are allowed, however, to keep selling existing stock and CCA treated wood is still available for industrial use. If you are already dealing with CCA treated wood, handle it with care and never burn it.

For a fact sheet from Health Canada on how to deal safely with CCA treated wood, visit: www.pmra-arla.gc.ca

For additional information on the handling of CCA treated wood, visit: www.ptw-safetyinfo.ca

4. Take action for ancient forests.

There are many ways to take action for ancient forests. Your purchases are one place to start. If your store or supplier does not stock FSC certified wood or community-based eco-timber, demand it. **See also 'Paper,' 'Floor coverings,' and 'Tissue products.'**

You can demand real solutions for ancient forests from governments and industry around the world. Greenpeace works in ancient forests including the Boreal Forest and the Great Bear Rainforest in Canada, the Amazon in Brazil, the Paradise Forests in Indonesia and Papua New Guinea and the Congo forests in Central Africa.

To take action for ancient forests and to find out more about Greenpeace's current campaigns, visit Greenpeace Canada at: www.greenpeace.ca and Greenpeace International at: www.greenpeace.org

Currently, the Ontario government is allowing clearcut logging on First Nations land in the Boreal Forest without meaningful consultation and in violation of established constitutional duties. The First Nations community of Grassy Narrows in northern Ontario is calling for a moratorium on logging on their territory. Although the province has recently opened up negotiations with the community, clearcut logging continues. For more information and to take action, visit: www.freegrassy.org

YARD (AND GARDEN)

OVERVIEW

We're going to extend the definition of yard to include the pots on your balcony, the hopeful plant on your only windowsill, the tiny plot under the fire escape. Whether you have a forest behind your house or a much-loved porch garden, growing is a good place to reduce your environmental impacts. And don't worry—your garden will be glorious!

Fact:

Almost three in ten households in Canada apply pesticides to their lawn or garden. 1

Must read:

You Grow Girl is a web resource and forum for lateral, organic gardeners who want to experiment, play and develop a refined appreciation for everything that grows. Visit: www.yougrowgirl.com

Simple step:

Start an organic gardening club on your street. Share cuttings, organic gardening tips and advice about native plants with your neighbours.

Where to start:

- ✲ Choose plants and grasses that are native to your area.
- ✲ Choose flowers, trees, ground cover and vegetables over a monoculture grass lawn.
- ✲ Choose certified organic potting soil and seeds.
- ✲ Avoid gas-powered equipment like lawn mowers and leaf blowers.
- ✲ Avoid pavement whenever possible.
- ✲ Choose organic pest and weed control.

Want more?

1. Start with a low-maintenance yard.

If you're starting from scratch, you have an exciting range of options. Your goal here: create a beautiful yard while reducing water use and eliminating the need for synthetic herbicides and pesticides. First, take some time to get to know your area and your garden. Which plants are native to your region? Do you have full sun, shade? Can you do without a lawn? Without pavement? Once you've figured out all the variables, make a plan.

The World Wildlife Fund has created a guide to creating and maintaining an organic garden. You can access it online at: www.wwf.ca

2. Choose plants native to your region.

In general, grass lawns should be avoided. A lawn is an unnatural ecosystem. Planting one plant species over a large area encourages weeds and pests.

Choose a variety of plants that are native to your region. [2]

3. Use less water.

✱ Whenever possible, let the rain water your yard.

✱ If you must water your lawn and garden, water early in the morning or at night to prevent evaporation. One inch of water a week is better than several short showers.

✱ Grow ground cover or use mulch in your garden to cut down on water use (it also helps to control weeds).

✱ Set your mower blades to high. The minimum height for grass is two and a half inches. Anything shorter is hard to maintain, encourages weeds and disease and requires more intervention. Longer grass also protects the roots, offering more shade and preventing water evaporation.

4. Choose natural ground cover over pavement and asphalt.

Natural groundcover absorbs water, while rainwater that lands on hard surfaces like pavement can drag toxins into lakes and rivers and overwhelm sewer systems during storms. Attempt to minimize surfaces like driveways and concrete walkways.

5. Avoid gas-powered lawn care equipment.

Gas-powered lawn equipment is a significant source of greenhouse gas emissions. Try using manual, electric or even solar-powered lawn equipment.

6. Avoid synthetic pesticides and herbicides.

Synthetic pesticides and herbicides are bad for the environment and dangerous for you and your family. Children in particular are vulnerable to the health effects of pesticides. According to the Sierra Club of Canada, over thirty-four million kilograms of pesticides are used annually across Canada. ₃ It's up to all of us to keep these dangerous toxics out of the environment. Here are a few ways to keep bugs and weeds away, chemical-free:

✱ Spend an evening outdoors weeding your lawn by hand early in the season.

✱ Companion planting is the cornerstone of organic gardening. The basic principle: put plants that pests hate next to the ones they love.

✱ Try putting a cone of birdseed in your garden. You can also plant flowers that attract birds. Birds can be more efficient than people at getting rid of bugs.

✱ There are a variety of organic pesticide and herbicide options. Try a few to see what works for you.

7. Choose organic potting soil and seedlings.

For your kitchen or balcony garden, consider organic potting soil. Organic seeds and seedlings are available for everything from artichokes to echinacea.

8. Demand strong chemical regulation in Canada and participate in community campaigns.

While some municipalities have taken the lead and banned pesticides, the federal government has failed to provide comprehensive legislation regulating chemicals in Canada. Demand strong, consistent chemical regulation from provincial, municipal and federal governments. Participate in community initiatives to go pesticide-free.

03

BIG ISSUES

CLIMATE CHANGE
OCEANS
ANCIENT FORESTS
TAR SANDS
BIOFUELS
NUCLEAR ENERGY

Environmental issues—in particular global environmental issues—can be difficult to understand. **First,** they are often tangled up in the complicated science of the natural world. **Second,** they are impossible to extricate from the intricate workings of governments, from the particular logic of international financial institutions and from history itself. **In this section,** we attempt to tease out some of the planet's most serious global environmental problems.

CLIMATE CHANGE

Life on earth is made possible by our atmosphere, the gases that envelop our planet like a blanket. The atmosphere—termed the 'great aerial ocean' by nineteenth-century British scientist Alfred Russel Wallace—regulates our climate, absorbing and tempering the sun's rays and protecting us from the frigid vacuum of outer space. It also provides us with the oxygen we breathe, and, in intimate concert with the oceans and the sun, cycles our water from river to ocean to rain and back again.

The atmosphere is made up of three primary gases—78 percent nitrogen, 20.9 percent oxygen and 0.9 percent argon. About 0.1 percent of the atmosphere consists of other, trace gases, some of which trap heat near the earth's surface. We call these heat-trapping gases greenhouse gases, and, although they make up only a tiny percentage of our atmosphere, they have enormous potential to influence our climate. Carbon dioxide, for example, accounts for only three parts per 10,000 of the atmosphere's gases but is the largest contributor to global warming. Other greenhouse gases include methane and nitrous oxide.

Most of the carbon dioxide in our atmosphere comes from natural sources. Carbon dioxide is created by the slow decay of organic matter. Animals also release carbon dioxide when we breathe (as opposed to plants, which, during the day, take in carbon dioxide and release oxygen). In addition, massive amounts of carbon dioxide are stored in the oceans, the earth's crust and in our forests—the oceans alone contain fifty times more carbon dioxide than the atmosphere. Now, for the first time in the planet's history, human activity is contributing significantly to the atmosphere's inventory of carbon dioxide, catalyzing—and continuing to fuel—a process scientists are terming 'climate change.'

At the beginning of the industrial revolution—around the year 1800—a relatively small group of countries began burning intense volumes of coal and, eventually, other fossil fuels like oil and gas, releasing long-stored carbon dioxide into the atmosphere. These are often termed 'anthropogenic' or 'human-made' emissions to distinguish them from naturally occurring greenhouse gases. It is estimated that, today, concentrations of carbon dioxide are more than one third higher than they were before the industrial revolution. Why? Well, in part because of how we lead our daily lives, particularly in rich countries. Every time you drive a car, take a plane, heat your home, flip a light switch or buy (almost any) consumer product, you are producing carbon dioxide.

This build-up of carbon dioxide and other human-generated greenhouse gases like methane and nitrous oxide is trapping heat close to the earth's surface, leading to a general warming trend in the planet's climate. According to the United Nations Intergovernmental Panel on Climate Change (IPCC), in 2005, the atmospheric concentration of carbon dioxide exceeded by far levels over the last 650,000 years. In addition, the annual growth rate of carbon dioxide concentrations was larger over the last ten years than it has been since scientists began continuous atmospheric measurements in 1960. According to the IPCC, the result is an 'unequivocal' warming of our climate system. Today, our world is hotter than it has been in two thousand years and scientists predict temperatures will continue to rise.

The consequences begin with the melting of ice sheets and glaciers, contributing to rising sea levels around the world. Average sea levels rose by ten to twenty centimetres through the 20th century. While it's impossible to know exactly how high sea levels might rise in the future, scientists are predicting an increase of somewhere between 3.5 to 34.6 inches—recent IPCC findings suggest sea level increases could be dramatically higher. Warming temperatures are also changing ecosystems around the world, affecting northern communities as sea ice melts, permafrost thaws and ice shelves disintegrate. Droughts are becoming more frequent as well. According to Greenpeace International, the global incidence of drought has doubled over the past thirty years.

Our world is already changing, but according to scientists, this is just the beginning. In the case of even a mild to moderate warming, we can expect

CLIMATE CHANGE

to see severe threats to people including flooding due to rising sea levels, the spread of disease and declines in agricultural production. At all scales of climate changé, countries with less infrastructure and fewer financial resources will suffer the most.

Climate change is happening now and its impacts are already apparent. And, if rich countries—the nations responsible for the bulk of historic anthropogenic emissions—do not act, future consequences will be catastrophic, in particular for countries without the resources to adapt to rapid changes in climate conditions. Currently, there is one international agreement in place designed to reduce global greenhouse gas emissions: the Kyoto Protocol on climate change, which was negotiated under the auspices of the United Nations. More than 170 countries—including Canada—have ratified the Kyoto Protocol, which calls for countries classified as industrial to reduce their greenhouse gas emissions to at least five percent below 1990 levels during the first commitment period of 2008 to 2012. While the Kyoto Protocol is only a beginning in the global fight against climate change, it is a crucial first step. Unfortunately, some large emitters—like the US—have refused to ratify the Kyoto Protocol. Others—like Canada—ratified the treaty and then proceeded to ignore their commitments.

Canadians have never been more concerned about climate change than they are right now. Unfortunately, Stephen Harper's Conservative government has made it clear that it will back away from the Kyoto Protocol. It's up to all Canadians to make—and keep—climate change an election issue.

Some good news: Greenpeace's Energy Revolution

In 2007, Greenpeace released a report called *Energy [R]evolution: A Sustainable World Energy Outlook*. The report, which outlines practical solutions for a clean energy future, was developed in conjunction with specialists from the Institute of Technical Thermodynamics at the German Aerospace Centre and more than thirty scientists and engineers from around the world. Some findings include:

* Renewable energy has the potential to deliver close to 70 percent of global electricity supply and 65 percent of global heat by 2050.

* Global carbon dioxide emissions can be cut by almost 50 percent within the next forty-three years while providing an affordable energy supply and maintaining steady worldwide economic development.

To read the full report, please visit: www.energyblueprint.info

Sources:

Greenpeace International. (www.greenpeace.org)

Intergovernmental Panel on Climate Change. 'Climate Change 2007: The Physical Science Basis. Summary for Policymakers.' (www.ipcc.ch)

Tim Flannery. *The Weathermakers*. HarperCollins. 2005.

Brain Laghi. *The Globe and Mail*. 'Climate concerns now top security and health.' January, 2007.

Dorrick Stow. *New Internationalist*. 'Climate Control.' January/February 2007.

OCEANS

Like the atmosphere, the ocean is an intimate part of our lives. We breathe out, and the ocean takes in our carbon dioxide. We breathe in, and the ocean's abundant plant life—called phytoplankton—uses photosynthesis to provide us with oxygen. In fact, the ocean is responsible for every second breath we take.

The ocean also plays a key role in regulating the climate, redistributing heat across the world's climatic zones with its currents. In addition, it helps keep global temperatures from spiking by storing massive amounts of carbon dioxide, holding fifty times more than the atmosphere itself and absorbing up to 40 percent of human-generated emissions.

On top of regulating our climate and providing us with oxygen, the ocean houses the most life-intensive ecosystems on the planet. It is estimated that 90 percent of the world's biomass lives in the ocean. From marine mammals to microscopic organisms, the ocean contains somewhere between 500,000 and one million distinct species, many of which humans depend on for protein. According to the United Nations Food and Agriculture Organization (FAO), approximately one billion people rely on fish as their main source of animal protein, with a much higher dependence in coastal areas. Overall, about 20 percent of the planet gets at least 20 percent of its animal protein from fish.

We are dependent on the ocean, but we know very little about it. Although we do know that the ocean floor, in some ways, has similar topography to the continents—mountains (called seamounts), volcanoes and canyons—we have more maps of the moon than we do of deep sea ecosystems. To date, only 0.0001 percent of the deep sea floor has been subject to biological investigation. We don't know what's there, but we're assaulting it all the same with a perfect storm of environmental problems that has led researchers from the US National Science Foundation to conclude that more than 40 percent of the ocean has been impacted by human activity and that no area at all has been left unaffected.

greenpeace living

greenpeace

While the ocean is affected by environmental issues from climate change to plastics dumping to agricultural chemicals to offshore drilling, relatively recent destructive fishing practices present a grave short-term threat to both ocean ecosystems and food security. Before the Second World War, fishing was largely restricted to coastal areas, which, for the most part, are mapped and managed—if inadequately—by national regulatory regimes. Later in the century, new technologies allowed industrial fishing vessels to harvest in deeper—uncharted and unregulated— waters, generating new forms of destruction and threatening smaller, local fisheries that operate closer to the coasts.

During the second half of the twentieth century, the global catch grew at a staggering rate. According to the FAO, world fishery production increased from 39.2 million tonnes in 1961 to 122.1 million tonnes in 1997. But, as Carl Safina and Carrie Brownstein point out in their comprehensive article about global fisheries, 'Fish or cut bait: solutions for our seas,' by around the early nineties real catches—as opposed to reported catches—were on the decline, a sure indication that the ocean's resources were reaching the breaking point.

Today, industrial fishing vessels are fitted out like giant factories with fish processing and packing plants and large-scale freezing systems. Fishing techniques like high seas bottom-trawling drag massive weighted nets across the ocean floor, destroying everything in their wake. Industrial fisheries also generate 'by-catch'—non-target species caught and killed by fishing nets. The results of this endless harvest are predictable. Approximately 29 percent of seafood species are considered collapsed—fished out to the point where they cannot reproduce themselves. Populations of top predators, a key indicator of ecosystem health, are disappearing quickly and 90 percent of large fish like tuna, swordfish, marlin, cod, halibut, skate and flounder have been fished out. The depletion of these top predator species can cause a shift in entire ocean ecosystems, as commercially valuable fish are replaced by smaller, plankton-feeding species like jellyfish.

OCEANS

As with most environmental problems, the consequences are asymmetrical. When it comes to declining fish stocks, people in rich countries are largely insulated—for now. Industrial fishing fleets in countries like the US and Japan—the two largest seafood importers in the world—have decimated many of their own fisheries. Now they are turning to relatively healthy fisheries in the Pacific and West Africa. In the Pacific, for example, a fleet of locally based vessels owned by both foreign and local companies catches about 200,000 tonnes of tuna each year. At the same time, increasing numbers of industrial fishing vessels are moving into the Pacific, taking about 1,800,000 tonnes—90 percent of the total catch—annually. The profit for Pacific nations from this bumper crop? Five percent or less of the $2 billion US market price for the fish.

We are at a crossroads when it comes to global fisheries management. As the world wakes up to the imminent crisis faced by the ocean and all those who depend on it, a number of solutions have been proposed. In 2006, a moratorium on high seas bottom-trawling was voted on at the United Nations. Unfortunately, it was defeated by countries like Iceland who placed the interests of their fishing fleets over the health of the oceans. Attempts have been made through international organizations like the International Whaling Commission (IWC) to enforce an existing global moratorium on commercial whaling. But, like most environmental agreements, there are no real enforcement mechanisms in place, and some countries continue the commercial whale hunt in violation of the moratorium.

There is one, comprehensive solution that addresses a number of issues including waste disposal, resource extraction, whaling and overfishing all at once: the establishment of a global network of marine reserves. We are used to zoning land for specific purposes. Now, marine scientists and NGOs like Greenpeace are saying it's time to do the same for the ocean. This means choosing key ocean areas and closing them off to extractive uses like industrial fishing and mining along with disposal activities. Marine reserves can, however, still allow for fishing. Some areas within the coastal zone may be opened to small-scale, non-destructive fisheries if this is decided upon with the full participation of local communities. In addition, marine reserves have the potential to help revitalize fisheries. Inside marine reserves, marine life populations increase in size and individuals live longer, grow larger and develop increased reproductive potential. As a result, adjacent fisheries can benefit from the spillover of healthy fish, eggs and larvae.

We have pushed both our atmosphere and our ocean to the breaking point. We—humanity—are hitting a wall: we need our atmosphere and our ocean to breathe, to eat, to provide us with a livable climate. Both climate change and ocean destruction must be addressed comprehensively and holistically by international and national governments. Before it's too late.

Sources:

Please note that much of the information for this section was taken, with kind permission, from the *New Internationalist* special issue, State of the World's Oceans (Jan./Feb. 2007).

To read the complete special issue, or to subscribe to the *New Internationalist*, please visit: www.newint.org

Additional information comes from Greenpeace International's Defending Our Oceans campaign (http://oceans.greenpeace.org)

Other sources include:

'A Global Map of Human Impact on Marine Ecosystems.' Benjamin S. Halpern et. al. *Science Magazine*. February, 2008.

Feeding the Future, edited by Andrew Heintzman and Evan Solomon. 'Fish or cut bait: solutions for our seas,' by Carl Safina and Carrie Brownstein. House of Anansi Press. 2006.

Food and Agriculture Organization of the United Nations: Fisheries Global Information System. (www.fao.org/figis)

ANCIENT FORESTS

Around 10,000 years ago, near the end of the last ice age, human beings started clearing land for agriculture and permanent settlements, beginning the slow, steady process of deforestation. (According to some scientists, around 8,000 years ago, these same activities kicked off the present cycle of human-influenced climate change.) Today, global deforestation has spiralled out of control. Half the forest area lost since the last ice age has disappeared over the past eighty years and half of that destruction took place over the last thirty years. Right now, human activity destroys a natural forest the size of a soccer field every two seconds. While climate change plays a strong role in the potential disappearance of plants and animals, deforestation is a virtual guarantee of extinction. Without habitat—with nowhere to live— many species simply will not survive. Right now, scientists predict that the planet is entering the sixth major extinction event in its history. This is the first extinction event to occur directly as a result of human activity.

According to a report by Greenpeace International, *Roadmap to Recovery: The world's last intact forest landscapes*, key threats to forest ecosystems around the world include illegal and destructive logging; forest clearing for agriculture and grazing land; infrastructure including roadways, pipelines and new settlements; mining for metals, petroleum and natural gas; damming for hydropower; over-hunting and climate change. Local indigenous communities, non-governmental organizations and even some governments have mounted diverse, strategic and effective responses to these many threats. Unfortunately, solutions—where they are implemented—are never global and rarely have the capacity to address entire ecosystems, which can spread across national boundaries and even—as with the Boreal Forest—across continents.

Greenpeace believes that ancient forest destruction is a global problem that requires global solutions (although, it must be emphasized that these solutions should be driven and defined by local communities). As a result, Greenpeace is calling for a moratorium on new industrial development in all intact forest landscapes. Governments can then use the moratorium— in the context of a process involving direction, participation and informed consent from indigenous communities and other local communities—to set up a global network to protect all forests with a high conservation value.

To this end, Greenpeace recently collaborated with a number of other non-governmental organizations to complete a global assessment of the planet's remaining intact ancient forests. Researchers set out to document intact forest landscapes—as opposed to small, fragmented patches of forest—for a simple reason. Forests must be at least several thousand continuous square kilometres to remain, in general, a viable habitat for plant and animal species. Large mammals like caribou, jaguars, bears, tigers and forest elephants, in particular, require large stretches of habitat to remain healthy. Bigger forests are also better able to weather the effects of climate change.

For the purpose of the map, Greenpeace defined ancient, intact forests as landscapes of at least 500 square kilometres, largely shaped by natural events and with no visible sign of significant human impact. Using these criteria, Greenpeace discovered that less than 10 percent of the planet's land area remains as intact forest landscapes. What's left consists largely of two major forest types: tropical rainforest and boreal forest. A full 44 percent of the planet's remaining intact forest landscapes are boreal forests in Russia, Alaska and Canada.

An astonishing percentage of the planet's ancients forests are in Canada. In total—including both the Boreal Forest that stretches across the northern part of the country and the Great Bear Rainforest on British Columbia's north coast—Canada is home to a full 26.6 percent of the planet's remaining intact forest landscapes. Unfortunately, Canada has one of the worst records in the world when it comes to ancient forest protection. Only 5.9 percent of the country's intact forest landscapes are currently under strict protection.

In Canada and around the world, national governments must—by using processes that are driven by indigenous communities and other local stakeholders—use binding legislation to take responsibility for ancient

ANCIENT FORESTS

forest preservation. They should also ban imports of illegally and destructively sourced wood and use, promote and encourage the development of Forest Stewardship Council (FSC) certified products (see 'Paper' for more information on FSC certification).

Internationally, the ancient forest equivalent of the Kyoto Protocol on climate change would be the Convention on Biological Diversity (CBD) which recognizes the need for sustainable development and was agreed to in principle by 150 governments at the Rio Earth Summit in 1992. Unfortunately, no real binding rules have come out of the CBD to date and we are left with no global framework for forest preservation. Both international and national governments must work together to implement comprehensive solutions to ancient forest destruction. It's up to citizens to make sure they step up to the plate.

Unless otherwise noted, most of the information in this briefing—including some wording—is taken directly from Greenpeace International's new report, *Roadmap to Recovery: The world's last intact forest landscapes* and from the related website: www.intactforests.org

Other sources include:

The Weathermakers. Tim Flannery. Toronto: HarperCollins. 2005.

Action Point

Currently, the Ontario government is allowing clearcut logging on First Nations land in the Boreal Forest without meaningful consultation and in violation of established constitutional duties. The First Nations community of Grassy Narrows in northern Ontario is calling for a moratorium on logging on their territory. Although the province has recently opened up negotiations with the community, clearcut logging continues. For more information and to take action, visit: www.freegrassy.org

TAR SANDS ·

In northern Alberta, under an area of Boreal Forest the size of the state of Florida, lie the tar sands, the second largest proven oil reserves in the world. Up until recently, the process of getting usable oil from the tar sands was considered too expensive. Now, as the price of oil continues to rise, oil companies are descending on northern Alberta, turning the tar sands into the largest industrial project on earth. They are also turning Canada into ground zero for global climate change. *Time Magazine* has described the tar sands as 'Canada's buried energy treasure' that 'could satisfy the world's demands for petroleum for the next century.' The UK newspaper *The Independent* describes them as 'the greatest environmental crime in history.'

The tar sands are a mixture of sand, clay and a heavy crude oil called bitumen. To get to the oil, companies like Exxon Mobil, Shell and Suncor clearcut huge chunks of ancient Boreal Forest and strip away layer after layer of earth. Bitumen that is close to the surface can be recovered by open pit mining, which involves the world's largest trucks—some up to three stories high. For the 80 percent of tar sands deposits buried too deeply to be mined, oil companies heat the mixture 'in situ' or in place—they literally cook the earth. This process usually involves pumping steam underground, which loosens up the thick oil and allows it to rise to the surface. After the bitumen is extracted, it must go through an extensive refining process before it can be used as fuel.

All of this takes energy. By the time usable oil is produced from the tar sands, oil companies have generated up to five times more greenhouse gas emissions than conventional oil extraction. And this does not take into account the greenhouse gas emissions generated during end use (by cars, trucks, etc.). Right now, most of the energy that powers the tar sands is coming from natural gas, although industry and government are considering other options, including nuclear power.

Once the oil is out of the ground, 70 percent of it goes directly to the United States. Increasingly, Canada is seen by US policy makers as a 'secure' source of oil. And, because of a clause in the North American Free Trade

greenpeace
living

greenpeace

Agreement (NAFTA) restricting Canada's ability to cut back on future oil exports to the US, we don't seem to have much choice. The profits are, for the most part, leaving the country too. Huge swaths of the tar sands are owned by US companies—some experts predict they will retain 60 percent ownership by 2010. Currently, the government of Alberta charges oil companies only one percent royalties until they are able to make a profit.

Canada does, however, keep the environmental costs. The tar sands are Canada's fastest growing source of greenhouse gas emissions—if tar sands development continues, we will literally never be able to meet our commitments under the Kyoto Protocol on climate change. (The Kyoto Protocol calls for Canada to reduce emissions by six percent below 1990 levels by 2012 at the outside. Although Canada ratified the Kyoto Protocol in 2002, we are approximately 29 percent *above* 1990 greenhouse gas emissions today, with no reductions in sight.) If tar sands development continues, other greenhouse gas reduction initiatives in Canada will be effectively neutralized. By 2020, the tar sands will emit more than 141 million tonnes of greenhouse gas emissions.

And greenhouse gas emissions are only the beginning. It takes four barrels of fresh water from the Athabasca River to produce one usable barrel of oil (present production levels are about 1.25 million barrels per day). When the oil companies are done with the water, 90 percent of it is too polluted to be returned to the river, and is kept in toxic tailings ponds so large they can be seen from space. In the meantime, the toxic emissions from tar sands projects are polluting the air and the river itself. Recently, the First Nations community of Fort Chipewyan, which is downstream from the tar sands projects, has begun to publicize their concerns about the effects of water pollution on their health. Over the past few years they have noticed increased incidences of cancer and diseases like lupus and multiple sclerosis. There have also been reports of mutations in animals and fish in ecosystems downstream from tar sands projects.

TAR SANDS

There is some small measure of hope in all this. While the total area available for development is 149,000 square kilometres of ancient Boreal Forest, only 31 percent of the tar sands is currently covered by leasing agreements. (This could change fast—there were 60,125 applications for development projects in 2006 alone.) In the meantime, the tar sands are receiving an unprecedented amount of negative attention. News outlets around the world carry images of the clearcut forests, the giant open pit mines, the three-storey trucks, the hundreds of water fowl dying on the massive tailings ponds, the deformed fish. A groundswell of support for a check on tar sands development is growing across the country—even an oil industry lobby group is asking for a partial moratorium.

But a partial moratorium won't solve the impacts of tar sands development. Neither will nuclear power, or the use of electricity instead of steam for in situ mining, or even carbon capture and storage. Industry and government would have us believe that, when it comes to the impacts of energy extraction, the challenges are basically technical. It's not a question of reducing energy use, the argument goes, it's a question of innovation. But what we have on our hands in northern Alberta (and in Canada, and around the world) is not a failure of technology. It's a failure of political will. Governments should make reasonable decisions based on the best interests of citizens and the environment. When it comes to the tar sands, the only reasonable decision is to shut the whole thing down.

Sources:

Greenpeace Canada tar sands campaign.

Cbcnews.ca. 'Tories to spend $230M on clean energy technology.' January, 2007.

Right: Some of the toxic tailings ponds generated by the tar sands are so large they can be seen from space. (Photo, copyright, Pembina Institute)

BIOFUELS

For decades, industry and government have been asking technology to answer this question: how can we increase energy use and reduce greenhouse gas emissions at the same time? In response, technology has offered answers that come with their very own problems (think nuclear power), the latest of which is biofuel—gasoline made from crops like corn and wheat. The upside of biofuel is simple: food crops store carbon while they grow, taking greenhouse gases out of the atmosphere. The downsides are also simple. Biofuels may actually generate more greenhouse gas emissions than they save. They also increase the use of chemicals that pollute air and waterways. They are also made out of food.

Biofuel crops don't replace oil—they use it. Industrial agriculture requires massive inputs of fossil fuels to run farm equipment and transport food. Non-organic agriculture also uses petrochemicals in the form of fertilizers, pesticides and herbicides. As Michael Pollan writes in *The Omnivore's Dilemma*, every bushel of industrial corn requires between a quarter to a third of a gallon of oil. In the end, common wisdom has it that corn-based ethanol, when compared to oil, produces a savings in greenhouse gas emissions of only about 20 percent. The 20 percent figure, though, fails to take into account the carbon dioxide emitted when intact ecosystems are cleared to grow fuel. A recent study published in the journal *Science* estimates that, when land use changes are taken into account, corn ethanol could nearly double emissions over a thirty year period.

Since ethanol is supplied by industrial food producers, a large percentage of it comes from genetically engineered (GE) crops. In Canada, 50 percent of our corn is genetically engineered. That means that about half of the corn used for ethanol in Canada will be GE (the Harper government has announced that, by 2010, 5 percent of Canada's gasoline will be made from corn ethanol). Any increase of GE crops is bad news. GE crops spread, polluting traditional and organic fields and eating away at biodiversity.

But all of this pales in comparison to the food crisis that is unfolding in front of our eyes. In 2007, the United Nations special rapporteur on the right to food called biofuels a 'crime against humanity.' According to the Earth Policy Institute, the grain required to fill the gas tank of an SUV could feed one person for a year. Cars are already taking food out of the mouths of people. In 2008, approximately one-third of the US corn crop will go to biofuel. Right now, the United Nations World Food Programme (WFP) is warning that it lacks the resources to keep up with rising food prices which it attributes to factors including increased demand for animal feed, climate change and biofuels. The WFP says it's currently facing a half-billion dollar shortfall to meet 'existing assessed needs.' Biofuels have a death toll.

Biofuel is the answer to the wrong question. How do we ratchet up global energy use and reduce greenhouse gas emissions at the same time? We don't. Oil is finite, cropland is finite, climate change is in progress. No amount of technological innovation will erase these realities. In fact, as is the case with biofuels, it can make things much, much worse. Innovation in fuel alternatives—even those that hold promise, like biomass—aren't the

answer to climate change (or even to high oil prices). The answer is simple, so simple, there's little technical innovation required: reduce fuel consumption. This will, of course, require a different kind of innovation: innovation in policy. Which brings us to a question that actually needs to be asked: how can we encourage policy innovation in a market-driven paradigm (since the threat of planetary chaos doesn't seem to be doing the trick)? If we can't, there's no quick fix. It's time to adjust the paradigm itself.

Sources:

Greenpeace Canada biofuels campaign.

Greenpeace Canada. Steven Guilbeault, Éric Darier and Habiba Drizi. 'Feeding the world or cars: the future of biotechnology in Quebec.' June, 2007.

Greenpeace International. 'Technical backgrounder on genetically engineered corn in Canada.'

Earth Policy Institute (www.earth-policy.org/Updates/2006/Update55.htm)

Julian Borger. The Guardian. 'Feed the world? We are fighting a losing battle, UN admits.' February, 2008.

Peter Gorrie. Toronto Star. 'Biofuels not 'miracle' cure, studies say.' February, 2008.

Michael Grunwald. Time Magazine, 'The Clean Energy Scam.' March, 2008.

Kurt Kleiner. 'The backlash against biofuels.' Nature. December, 2007.

NUCLEAR ENERGY

The nuclear age began in July, 1945 when the US tested their first nuclear bomb near Alamogordo, New Mexico. Since then, countries around the world have acquired nuclear weapons, often concurrently and in close relationship with the development of civilian nuclear energy programs. Today, nuclear energy is promoted by the industry as 'friendly' technology, a stable source of energy and a viable response to climate change. In reality, nuclear energy comes with a complement of problems from nuclear waste to radioactive tritium emissions, from staggering cost overruns to frequent associations with nuclear weapons programs.

The problems with nuclear energy start at the very beginning of the nuclear cycle with uranium, a radioactive metal used as the fuel for both nuclear reactors and nuclear weapons. Three nations—Canada, Kazakhstan and Australia—are responsible for 58 percent of the world's supply of raw uranium. Right now, Canada is the largest producer, with about one-third of global production. Although all of Canada's current uranium comes from mining operations (uranium is mostly mined from rock) in northern Saskatchewan, aggressive exploration is taking place in Ontario and northern Quebec.

When it's left in the ground, most of uranium's radioactivity is safely locked away. When it's disturbed by exploration or mining, radioactive particles can be released into the air and water and can pose serious health risks when ingested or inhaled. Once mined, uranium is processed into fuel at one of five facilities in Canada, all of which are in Ontario, and some of which are housed in major population centres, including a facility at a busy intersection in the west end of Toronto. About 15 to 20 percent of Canada's processed uranium is used domestically. The rest is shipped to nuclear facilities across the globe.

Which brings us to the nuclear reactors themselves, 439 around the world, generating approximately 15 percent of global electricity (as opposed to energy—nuclear power does not provide central heating or hot water). In Canada, our twenty-two aging reactors (twenty in Ontario, one in Quebec and one in New Brunswick), many of which have been shut down due to

greenpeace
living

greenpeace

poor performance and safety problems, provide 14 percent of Canada's electricity supply (45 percent in Ontario). They've also cost tax-payers approximately $20 billion in government subsidies to Atomic Energy of Canada Limited since 1952, generated 40,000 tonnes of high-level radioactive waste and released the highest rates of tritium (radioactive water and water vapour produced by the nuclear process) in the world into our lakes and air.

The most apocalyptic risks of nuclear power are well-known. In 1986, an explosion and fire at a nuclear plant in Chernobyl in the Ukraine spread a radioactive cloud across a massive area of Europe and has been responsible for countless deaths from cancer and other radiation related illnesses. Following the disaster at Chernobyl, many countries turned their backs on nuclear power. In 1987, Italy abandoned nuclear power completely and has since closed all of its reactors. In 2000, Germany committed to phasing out nuclear energy in favour of renewables like wind power. Germany's then environment minister Jurgen Trittin said that phasing out nuclear power was "a logical response to Chernobyl." In Canada, political leaders are showing no such prudence. In Ontario alone, the government is planning on spending $40 billion to both refurbish and rebuild the province's aging reactors and build new ones. In New Brunswick, the government is currently rebuilding the Point Lepreau nuclear station. In Quebec, the government will decide by the end of 2008 whether or not to refurbish the reactor at Gentilly 2. Bruce Power is even proposing a nuclear plant to help power the tar sands in northern Alberta.

Nuclear power is polluting, unsafe and unimaginably expensive. But it might be even more dangerous as a red herring, a detour on the path to reducing global greenhouse gas emissions. Right now, industry and some governments are touting nuclear power as a solution to global climate change. In fact, the opposite is true. On a global scale, nuclear power undermines action on climate change by taking away from practical, easy-to-deploy solutions like wind power, solar power and local generation. Even if one new large reactor came online every two weeks until 2030, global carbon dioxide emissions would only be reduced by less than five percent. Given that even countries with established nuclear programs, like Canada, typically take more than a decade to construct a new reactor, even a modest reduction in greenhouse gas emissions through nuclear power is unrealistic.

By contrast, proven renewable energy technologies are available now, can be constructed and brought online quickly and provide immediate cuts in greenhouse gas emissions. For example, construction time for a new wind turbine has fallen to only two weeks, with an associated planning period of between one and two years. In 2007, Greenpeace and the European Renewable Energy Council teamed up to produce Energy [R]evolution, an exhaustive report with input from more than thirty scientists and engineers around the world. The report clearly demonstrates that it is possible to maintain economic growth, achieve more universal access to energy and phase out both nuclear energy and fossil fuels. Solutions exist. Nuclear power is not one of them. Let's hope our governments demonstrate the political will and respect for future generations to adopt the sustainable energy solutions that already exist.

Sources:

Greenpeace Canada nuclear energy campaign.

Greenpeace International. 'Briefing: Nuclear Power Energy Insecurity.' 2008.

Bernard Simon. *The New York Times*. 'Ontario Considers Building a Nuclear Plant.' June 18th, 2004.

Right: Lyle Thurston, a Greenpeace founder, was the ship's doctor on the original Greenpeace voyage to stop US nuclear testing in Amchitka, Alaska in 1971. Lyle Thurston, 1937-2008. He will be missed.

Action Point

At press time, the Ontario government was allowing uranium and other mineral exploration on the traditional land of Indigenous peoples without consultation and in violation of established constitutional rights. For more information and to take action, visit: www.greenpeace.org/canada/en/recent/moratorium-on-uranium-exploration, www.amnesty.ca/urgentappeal/ardoch and www.ccamu.ca

04

RESOURCES

EVERYDAY ACTIVIST TIPS
RESOURCES FOR EVERYDAY ACTIVISTS
CERTIFICATIONS
END NOTES

Taking political action is one of the most meaningful things you can do for the planet. In this section, you will find some of the resources and strategies you need to be an everyday activist.

EVERYDAY ACTIVIST TIPS

1. You and your political representatives. Keep a quick reference sheet with contact information for your school trustee, your city councillor, your provincial representative and your member of parliament. Also, take note of relevant provincial and federal ministers like the minister of the environment and the minister of natural resources. Politicians need to know that their constituencies care about—and are personally bound up in—labour, social and environmental issues. It's easy to find your local politicians online. They are your representatives—you have a right to tell them what you think! ·

2. The power of the toll-free number. Most products have a toll-free number right on the back. Many big brands have a comment box on their website. When a question or concern occurs to you, take a moment to call or write. If you send an email, forward it to a few friends suggesting they do the same. Remember to keep your letters short, clear and polite.

3. Explore civil society. Once you've engaged government and industry, there is a third sector that can help you address environmental concerns. Civil society is made up of groups of concerned citizens, working independently to effect change. Consider volunteering with an environmental group. Many organizations and citizens' groups also have electronic newsletters that will deliver activist ideas straight to your inbox.

To sign up for Greenpeace's electronic newsletter, please visit:
www.greenpeace.org/canada/en/enewsletter

Consider joining Greenpeace's team of volunteers. Visit:
www.greenpeacevolunteers.ca

Right: Everyone can be an activist. You can start by sending one email or making one phone call a week.

greenpeace
living

RESOURCES FOR EVERYDAY ACTIVISTS

CLEANING

Eco labels: Information from the Consumer's Union: www.eco-labels.org

Energy-efficient appliances: www.oee.nrcan.gc.ca/residential/personal

Environmental Choice certified cleaning products (Government of Canada): www.environmentalchoice.com

Greener dry cleaners in Canada: www.c2p2online.com/main.php3?section =139&doc_id=295CLOTHING

Hanging clothes to dry: www.laundrylist.org

Toxic chemicals in cleaning products: Information from the Labour Environmental Alliance Society: www.leas.ca/Toxins-in-Household-Products.htm

CLOTHING AND FABRIC

Campaigns and information on labour rights and working conditions in the garment industry: www.cleanclothes.org, www.maquilasolidarity.org

Clothing made under ethical conditions: Sweat Free Communities has compiled a 'Shop with a conscience' guide of garments produced under fair labour conditions: www.sweatfree.org/shopping. The union Unite Here also offers information on union-made clothing: www.unitehere.org/buyunion

Ethical buying policies in workplaces: www.maquilasolidarity.org/nosweat Student campaigns against sweatshops: www.studentsagainstsweatshops.org

Shopping for organic cotton clothing: www.organicexchange.org/consumer_mark etplace.php

ELECTRONICS

Energy-efficient electronics: www.oee.nrcan.gc.ca/residential/personal /index.cfm?attr=0

Greener computer certifications: http://svtc.igc.org/cleancc/greendesign

Greenpeace Guide to Greener Electronics: www.greenpeace.org/greener electronics

Manufacturer recycling programs: www.epsc.ca/r_links.html

Solar-powered chargers: www.treehugger.com/files/2006/10/solar_ chargers_1.php

Workplace recycling donation programs (Government of Canada): www.ope.ic.gc.ca/Default.asp?lang=en

ENERGY (AT HOME)

Carbon offset programs:
www.davidsuzuki.org/Climate_Change/W
hat_You_Can_Do/carbon_neutral.asp

Compact fluorescent light bulbs:
www.oee.nrcan.gc.ca/publications/infosou
rce/pub/home/Household_Lighting_Sectio
n4.cfm

Energy-saving tips for home:
www.oee.rncan.gc.ca/residential/personal
/home-improvement.cfm?attr=4

Energy-efficient appliances:
www.oee.nrcan.gc.ca/equipment/english/
page9.cfm

Rebates for energy efficiency measures:
www.oee.nrcan.gc.ca/energystar/english/
consumers/rebate.cfm

**Rebates for energy efficiency measures
on mortgage loan insurance:**
www.cmhc-
schl.gc.ca/en/co/moloin/moloin_008.cfm

Reducing energy bills:
www.gca.ca/indexcms

Solar power: www.cansia.ca

Wind power: www.canwea.ca

FLOOR COVERINGS

**Environmental Choice certified flooring
(Government of Canada):**
www.environmentalchoice.com

Forest Stewardship Council certification:
www.fsccanada.org

Greener flooring options:
www.saferproducts.org

**Greener flooring options
(Government of Canada):**
www.pwgsc.gc.ca/realproperty/text/pubs_
ercr/appendix_a4-e.html

Polyvinyl chloride:
www.healthybuilding.net,
www.pvcinformation.org

Rediscovered Wood certification:
www.rainforest-alliance.org

Rugmark certification:
www.rugmark.org

RESOURCES FOR EVERYDAY ACTIVISTS

FOOD

Community gardens in Canada:
www.communitygarden.org/links.php

Farm workers in Canada: 'El Contrato' - Min Sook Lee's excellent documentary on farm workers in Ontario's tomato industry. For more information, visit: www.nfb.ca. For more information and to write your MP to demand justice for farm workers in Canada, visit: www.justicia4migrantworkers.org

Food production: 'Our Daily Bread' - Nikolaus Geyrhalter's documentary about the world of industrial food production (ourdailybread.at). *The Omnivore's Dilemma* by Michael Pollan. Penguin Press. 2006. *Stolen Harvest: the hijacking of the global food supply* by Vandana Shiva. South End Press. 2000.

Organic growing:
Learn about organic farming and read about the Saskatchewan Organic Directorate's lawsuit against Monsanto for contaminating organic crops. www.saskorganic.com

Shopping for organic food in Canada:
www.cog.ca/buyorganic.htm, www.eatwellguide.org

Vegetarian recipes:
www.vegcooking.com

PAINTS, FINISHES AND ADHESIVES

Environmental Choice certified paints, finishes and adhesives (Government of Canada):
www.environmentalchoice.com

Lead-based paint: Information from Health Canada: www.hc-sc.gc.ca/iyh-vsv/prod/paint-peinture_e.html Information from Canada Mortgage and Housing Corporation: www.cmhc-schl.gc.ca (search for lead)

Paints and finishes (Government of Canada):
www.pwgsc.gc.ca/realproperty/text/pubs_ercr/appendix_a9-e.html

PAPER AND PRINTING

Eco-friendly paper:
www.marketsinitiative.org/resources/paper-database

Environmental policies in workplaces:
www.marketsinitiative.org

Forest friendly tissue products:
http://tissue.greenpeace.ca

Forest Stewardship Council certification:
www.fsccanada.org

Paper impacts calculator from Environmental Defense:
www.edf.org/papercalculator

PLASTICS AND NON-STICK COATINGS

PVC toys: www.hc-sc.gc.ca/ahc-asc/media/advisories-avis/1998/1998_85bk1_e.html

Non-stick cookware: www.hc-sc.gc.ca/iyh-vsv/prod/cook-cuisinier_e.html

greenpeace
living

greenpeace

SEAFOOD

Bottom-trawling:
www.oceans.greenpeace.org/en/our-oceans/bottom-trawling

Mercury advisories:
www.oceansalive.org/eat.cfm?subnav=he althalerts

Ocean issues in Canada:
www.greenpeace.ca/oceans

Shopping for sustainable seafood:
www.greenpeace.ca/redlist
www.seachoice.org

SHOPPING

Eco-labels: www.eco-labels.org

Fair Trade in Canada: www.transfair.ca

Fair Trade certified suppliers:
www.ifat.org

TOILETRIES

Shopping for cosmetics:
www.ewg.org/reports/skindeep

Toxics in toiletries:
www.safecosmetics.org
www.lesstoxicguide.ca

TRANSPORTATION

Carpooling: www.carpool.ca

Fuel efficiency ratings for passenger vehicles:
www.oee.nrcan.gc.ca/transportation/personal

Idling:
www.oee.nrcan.gc.ca/transportation/pers onal/idling/stop-idling.cfm?attr=0

WASTE

Composting: Composting information from Environment Canada:
www.ns.ec.gc.ca/udo/paydirt.html

Composting Council of Canada:
www.compost.org/AboutComposting.html

Waste reduction in workplaces:
www.wrwcanada.com/resourcesB.htm

WATER

Ecological water purification:
www.oceanarks.org

Privatization:
www.navdanya.org/earthdcracy/water
www.canadians.org

Water in Canada: www.eausecours.org

WOOD

Forest Stewardship Council certification:
www.fsccanada.org

Handling Chromated Copper Arsenate treated wood: www.pmra-arla.gc.ca/english/pdf/fact/fs_cca-e.pdf
and www.ptw-safetyinfo.ca/cca.htm

Rediscovered Wood certification:
www.rainforest-alliance.org

YARD (AND GARDEN)

Organic gardening:
Web resources for organic gardeners:
www.yougrowgirl.com

CERTIFICATIONS

Environmental certifications

Choosing products selected by
credible certification programs
is a great way to reduce your
environmental impacts. On the
facing page, you'll find the
symbols and certifications
recommended in this guide.

Ancient forest friendly.
Applies to paper, books and
magazines. More information:
ancientforestfriendly.com

Fair Trade. Applies to
products including coffee, tea,
chocolate, cotton and roses.
More information: transfair.ca

**SmartWood Rediscovered
Wood.** Applies to recycled
and rediscovered wood
products. More information:
rainforest-alliance.org

Environmental Choice.
Applies to a variety of
products. More information:
environmentalchoice.com

ENERGY STAR. Applies to
a variety of products including
electronics and appliances.
More information: oee.nrcan.gc.ca

Rugmark. Applies to
rugs. More information:
rugmark.org

Forest Stewardship Council.
Applies to paper, tissue
products and wood. More
information: fsccanada.org

END NOTES

Top Tips

1 Consumer's Guide to Effective
Environmental Choices - Union of
Concerned Scientists. Michael Brower,
Warren Leon. New York: *Three Rivers Press*.
1999.

2 *Worldwatch Institute*. July, 2003.
(www.worldwatch.org/node/1770)

3 Diet, Energy and Global Warming (paper).
Published in *Earth Interactions*, Volume 10
(2006). Gideon Eshel, Pamela A. Martin
(University of Chicago). 2006.

4 National Inventory Report: Greenhouse
Gas Sources and Sinks in Canada 1990-
2005. Published by *Environment Canada*.
April 2007.

Cleaning

1 The Inside Story: A Guide to Indoor Air
Quality. Published by the *US Environmental
Protection Agency and the US Consumer
Product Safety Commission, Office of
Radiation and Indoor Air*. April, 1995. EPA
Document # 402-K-93-007.
(www.epa.gov/iaq/pubs/insidest.html#Look5)

2 Label Index. Eco-labels (eco-labels.org).
(www.eco-labels.org/label.cfm?LabelID=292)

3 What's In, What's Out: A Rating of Dry
Cleaning Methods Currently in Use in the
US (fact sheet). Published by *Greenpeace
US*. June, 2003.
(www.greenpeace.org/raw/content/usa/p
ress/reports/what-s-in-what-s-out-a-
ratin.pdf)

Other sources

Consumer's Guide to Effective
Environmental Choices - Union of
Concerned Scientists. Michael Brower,
Warren Leon. New York: *Three Rivers Press*.
1999.

Household cleaning supplies (product
report). *The Green Guide*. Updated, 2006.
(www.thegreenguide.com/reports/product.
mhtml?id=15)

Petrochemicals in cleaners? *The Green
Guide*. Emily Main. 2006.
(www.thegreenguide.com/doc/ask/petrol
eum)

Primer on Volatile Organic Compounds.
Published by *Pollution Probe*. Doug Harper,
Olivia Nugent. 2005.
(www.pollutionprobe.org)

Stepping Lightly on the Earth. Published by
Greenpeace Canada, circa 1998.

Clothing

1 Update on Genetically Engineered Cotton.
*International Cotton Advisory Committee
Recorder*, Volume XXII, Number 2.
Published by the *International Cotton
Advisory Committee*. June, 2004.
(www.icac.org/cotton_info/tis/biotech/doc
uments/recorderdocs/june_04.pdf)

2 Government Measures Affecting Cotton
Production and Trade (presentation).
International Cotton Advisory Committee.
Terry Townsend, ICAC Executive Director.
July, 2004. (www.cotton-
forum.org/docs/presentations/1.1-en.pdf)

3 Global statistic on genetically engineered
cotton calculated using data from the
following two sources: Update on

Genetically Engineered Cotton.
*International Cotton Advisory Committee
Recorder*, Volume XXII, Number 2.
Published by the *International Cotton
Advisory Committee*. June, 2004. AND
Adoption of Genetically Engineered Crops
in the US (data set). *US Department of
Agriculture Economic Research Service*.
(www.ers.usda.gov/data/biotechcrops)

4 The Deadly Chemicals in Cotton (report).
Published by the *Environmental Justice
Foundation* with *Pesticide Action Network
UK*. 2007. (www.pan-uk.org)

5 Pesticides: Health and Safety (web
resource). *US Environmental Protection
Agency*.
(www.epa.gov/pesticides/health/human.ht
m#1)

6 Pesticides and Pesticide Management in
Canada (fact sheet). *World Wildlife Fund*.
(www.wwfcanada.org/satellite/prip/factsh
eets/pesticide-management.html)

7 Cultivating Poverty: the Impact of US
Cotton Subsidies on Africa (briefing paper).
Published by *Oxfam International*. Kevin
Watkins with Jung-ui Sul. 2002.
(www.oxfam.org.uk/what_we_do/issues/tr
ade/bp30_cotton.htm)

8 What is a Sweatshop and Where are
Sweatshops Found? (FAQ). *Sweatshop
Watch*. (www.sweatshopwatch.org)

9 Green Tips: Environmental Ideas in Action
(web resource). *Union of Concerned
Scientists*. 2000.
(www.ucsusa.org/publications/greentips/6
00-dressing-green.html)

10 Digging up Bamboo's Dark Side (article).
Adria Vasil. *Now Magazine*. October 25th,
2007.

11 Green Tips: Environmental Ideas in Action
Union of Concerned Scientists. 2000.

Other sources

Bamboo Bonanza (article). Daphne Gordon.
Toronto Star. November 25th, 2006.

Biotech Crop Growers Moving into Clothing
Industry (article). Paul Elias. *USA Today*. July
19th, 2006.

Biotech Fashion Show Highlights Designer
Fashions Made with Biotech Fabric (press
release). *Biotechnology Industry Association*.
July, 2006.
(www.bio.org/news/newsitem.asp?id=2006
_0713_02)

Green is the New Black. Leo Hickman.
The Guardian. October 7th, 2004.

Is Fair Trade Good for the Garment Industry?
(report). Published by the *Maquila Solidarity
Network*. 2006. (www.maquilasolidarity.org)

NRC Works to Improve Hemp Technology
(web resource). *National Resource Council*.
2004. (www.nrc-
cnrc.gc.ca/education/innovations/sti-
inno_hemp_e.html)

Electronics

1 Exporting Harm: The High-tech Trashing
of Asia (report). Published by the *Basil
Action Network* and the *Silicon Valley
Toxics Coalition*. 2002. (www.ban.org/E-
waste/technotrashfinalcomp.pdf)

2 Toxic Tech: Pulling the Plug on Dirty
Electronics (report). Published by
Greenpeace International. May, 2005.
(www.greenpeace.org/raw/content/china/
en/press/reports/toxic-tech-puling-the-
plug-o.pdf)

END NOTES

[3] Human Activity and the Environment: Solid Waste. *The Daily* published by *Statistics Canada*. December 2nd, 2005. (www.statcan.ca/Daily/English/051202/d051202b.htm)

[4] 12 Steps (web resource). *Greenpeace International* climate change campaign. (www.greenpeace.org/international/campaigns/climate-change/take_action/12_steps)

Other sources

Greenpeace Guide to Greener Electronics (report). *Greenpeace International*, toxics campaign. (www.greenpeace.org/international/news/green-electronics-guide-ewaste250806)

Where Does E-Waste End Up? (web resource). *Greenpeace International*, toxics campaign. (www.greenpeace.org/international/campaigns/toxics/electronics/where-does-e-waste-end-up)

Energy at home

[1] Climate Change 2007: The Physical Science Basis (summary for policymakers). *Intergovernmental Panel on Climate Change*. 2007. (www.ipcc.ch/SPM2feb07.pdf)

[2] National Inventory Report: Greenhouse Gas Sources and Sinks in Canada 1990-2005. Published by *Environment Canada*. April 2007.

[3] Ibid

[4] Statistics in this section from the National Inventory Report: Greenhouse Gas Sources and Sinks in Canada 1990-2005 (see previous).

[5] 12 Steps (web resource). *Greenpeace International* climate change campaign. (www.greenpeace.org/international/campaigns/climate-change/take_action/12_steps)

[6] Diet, Energy and Global Warming (paper). Published in *Earth Interactions*, Volume 10 (2006). Gideon Eshel, Pamela A. Martin (University of Chicago). 2006.

[7] Livestock a major threat to environment (report summary). Published by the *United Nations Food and Agriculture Organization*. November, 2006. (www.fao.org/newsroom/en/news/2006/1000448/index.html)

[8] *Greenpeace Canada* energy campaign. Dave Martin, campaigner coordinator. (www.greenpeace.org/canada/en/campaigns/climate-and-energy)

Other sources

Canadian Solar Industries Association (www.cansia.ca)

Greenpeace Canada energy campaign (www.greenpeace.org/canada/en/campaigns/climate-and-energy)

Green Communities Canada - Advice in conversation from Kai Millyard. (www.gca.ca/indexcms)

Natural Resources Canada - Office of Energy Efficiency (oee.nrcan.gc.ca)

Consumer and Industrial Lighting (web resource). *General Electric*. (www.gelighting.com/na/home_lighting/ask_us/faq_compact.htm)

Hot water burns like fire (web resource).
Canadian Health Network.
(www.canadian-health-
network.ca/servlet/ContentServer?cid=1126
033676226&pagename=CHN-
RCS/CHNResource/CHNResourcePageTem
plate&c=CHNResource)

Hot water burns like fire: Discussion paper
on tap water scalds prevention (overview).
Safe Kids Canada.
(www.sickkids.ca/SKCPublicPolicyAdvocacy
/section.asp?s=Tap+Water+Scalds&sID=13
747)

What you can do: Go carbon neutral (web
resource). *David Suzuki Foundation.*
(www.davidsuzuki.org/climate_change/wh
at_you_can_do/carbon_neutral.asp)

Floor coverings

1 The Environmentally Responsible
Construction and Renovation Handbook
(Appendix A). Published by *Public Works
and Government Services Canada.* March,
2000. See: 'Flexible vinyl flooring.'
(www.pwgsc.gc.ca/realproperty/text/pubs
_ercr/toc-e.html)

2 The Case of Rugmark. Published by the
*United Nations Development Program,
India.* Aparna Ravi. 2001. (www.unp.org/in)

Other sources

Eco-tips at Home (web resource).
Greenpeace Australia.
(www.greenpeace.org/australia/take-
action/live-greener/home)

An Architect's Guide for Sustainable Design
of Office Buildings. Published by *Public
Works and Government Services Canada.*
(www.pwgsc.gc.ca/realproperty/text/pubs
_archguide/pubs_archguide_toc-e.html)

Food

1 Greenpeace Shopper's Guide: How to
Avoid Genetically Engineered Foods.
Published by *Greenpeace Canada* genetic
engineering campaign. 2004.

2 Monsanto's 7 Deadly Sins (fact sheet).
Published by *Greenpeace International*
genetic engineering campaign. August,
2006.

3 *Worldwatch Institute.* July, 2003.
(www.worldwatch.org/node/1770)

4 Feed the world? We are fighting a losing
battle, UN admits (article). Julian Borger.
The Guardian. February 26th, 2008.

5 Diet, Energy and Global Warming (paper).
Published in *Earth Interactions,* Volume 10
(2006). Gideon Eshel, Pamela A. Martin
(University of Chicago). 2006.

6 Water - More Nutrition Per Drop: Towards
Sustainable Production and Consumption
Patterns in a Rapidly Changing World
(report). Commissioned by the Swedish
government and produced by the
Stockholm Water Institute and the
*International Water Management
Institute.* 2004.

7 Livestock a major threat to environment
(report summary). Published by the *United
Nations Food and Agriculture
Organization.* November, 2006.
(www.fao.org/newsroom/en/news/2006/1
000448/index.html)

8 Eating up the Amazon (report). Published
by *Greenpeace International.* April, 2006.
(www.greenpeace.org/raw/content/intern
ational/press/reports/eating-up-the-
amazon.pdf)

END NOTES

Other sources

Genetically Engineered Crops and an
Ecologically and Socially Sustainable
Agriculture (Greenpeace report). Éric Darier,
Ph.D., Frédéric Martel. 2005.

Meat Eaters Soak Up the World's Water
(article). *The Guardian*. October 7th, 2004.

The No Nonsense Guide to Fair Trade.
Oxford: *New Internationalist Publications
Inc*. David Ransom. 2001. (www.newint.org)

The Omnivore's Dilemma: A Natural
History of Four Meals. Michael Pollan. New
York: *Penguin Press*. 2006.

Packaging

[1] Irish Bag Tax Hailed a Success (article).
BBC News. August 20th, 2002.

Other sources

Paper or Plastic: Searching for Solutions to
an Overpackaged World. Daniel Imhoff.
San Francisco: *Sierra Club Books*. 2005.

Paint, finishes and adhesives

[1] Good Stuff? - Paints and Varnishes (web
resource). *Worldwatch Institute*.
(www.worldwatch.org/node/1496)

[2] Primer on Volatile Organic Compounds
(report). Published by *Pollution Probe*. Doug
Harper, Olivia Nugent. 2005.
(www.pollutionprobe.org)

[3] An Introduction to Indoor Air Quality,
Organic Gases (web resource). *US
Environmental Protection Agency*.
(www.epa.gov/iaq/voc.html#Levels%20in%
20Homes)

[4] Proposed Indoor Air Quality Guidelines
for Formaldehyde (report). *Health Canada*.
(see section 3.2.2) (www.hc-sc.gc.ca/ewh-
semt/pubs/air/formaldehyde/sources_e.ht
ml#2_2)

[5] Lead-based Paint (fact sheet). *Health
Canada*. (www.hc-sc.gc.ca/iyh-
vsv/prod/paint-peinture_e.html)

Other sources

Eco-tips at Home (web resource).
Greenpeace Australia.
(www.greenpeace.org/australia/take-
action/live-greener/home)

The Environmentally Responsible
Construction and Renovation Handbook
(Appendix A). Published by *Public Works
and Government Services Canada*. March,
2000. See: 'Paints and coatings.'
(www.pwgsc.gc.ca/realproperty/text/pubs
_ercr/appendix_a9-e.html)

Lead in paint, dust and soil (web resource).
US Environmental Protection Agency.
(http://www.epa.gov/lead/pubs/leadinfo.h
tm#facts)

Lead in Your Home: A Parent's Reference
Guide (guide). *US Environmental Protection
Agency*. 1998.
(www.epa.gov/lead/pubs/leadrev.pdf)

Paper and printing

[1] All paper facts in this section
courtesy of the *Markets Initiative*.
(www.marketsinitiative.org)

Plastics and non-stick coatings

1 Bottled Water: Pouring Resources Down the Drain (Eco-Economy update). *Earth Policy Institute*. February, 2006. (www.earth-policy.org/Updates/2006/Update51.htm)

2 Coming to Terms with the Peril of Non-Stick Products. The *Globe and Mail*. Martin Mittelstaedt. May 29th, 2006. (www.theglobeandmail.com/servlet/story/RTGAM.20060529.chemicals-nonstick29/BNStory/specialScienceandHea lth)

3 Canaries in the Kitchen (report). *Environmental Working Group*. 2003. (www.ewg.org/reports/toxicteflon/es.php)

4 Are Plastic Products Coated in Peril?. The *Globe and Mail*. Martin Mittelstaedt. May 31st, 2006. (www.theglobeandmail.com/servlet/story/RTGAM.20060531.wxchemicals-plastics/BNStory/specialScienceandHealth)

5 PVC Alternatives Database: Greenpeace Pyramid of Plastics (web resource). *Greenpeace International* toxics campaign. (http://archive.greenpeace.org/toxics/pvcd atabase/bad.html)

6 Ibid

7 Ibid

Other sources

Corn Plastic to the Rescue. *Smithsonian Magazine*. Elizabeth Royle. August, 2006.

Smart Plastics Guide (fact sheet). *Institute for Agriculture and Trade Policy*. (www.environmentalobservatory.org/library.cfm?refid=77083#search=%22smart%20pla)

Seafood

1 Fish Stock Face Collapse 'Within Our Lifetime'. The *Globe and Mail*. Alex Dobrota. November 3rd, 2006.

Other sources

Greenpeace Canada oceans campaign.

SeaChoice. (www.seachoice.org)

Shopping

1 Retail Trade by Province and Territory (table). *Statistics Canada*. (http://www40.statcan.ca/l01/cst01/trad17a .htm?sdi=retail)

2 Food Consumption, 2004. *The Daily* published by *Statistics Canada*. May 26th, 2005. (www.statcan.ca/Daily/English/050526/d0 50526c.htm) (This statistic represents combined average consumption of beef and pork in 2004.)

3 Greenpeace Shopper's Guide to Ancient Forest Friendly Tissue Products. *Greenpeace Canada* forests campaign. (www.greenpeace.org/canada/en/campai gns/boreal)

4 Waterproof 2: Canada's Drinking Water Report Card. *Sierra Legal Defence Fund*. 2006. (www.sierralegal.org/reports/waterproof.II. report.pdf)

END NOTES

Other sources

The No Nonsense Guide to Fair Trade.
Oxford: *New Internationalist Publications Inc*. David Ransom. 2001. (www.newint.org)

Special events.

1 Saying it with Flowers and Saving the Planet. The *Globe and Mail*. Oliver Moore. February 13th, 2007.

2 How Green was My Wedding? *New York Times*. February 11th, 2007.

Tissue products

1 Facts in this section taken from:

Greenpeace Shopper's Guide to Ancient Forest Friendly Tissue Products.
Greenpeace Canada forests campaign. (www.greenpeace.org/canada/en/campaigns/boreal)

Greenpeace Canada forests campaign. Richard Brooks, campaign coordinator.

Toiletries

1 Toxic Shock: Part 1. The *Globe and Mail*. Martin Mittelstaedt. May 27th, 2006.

2 Conversations with Anne Wordsworth, toxics researcher and co-author of *Cancer: 101 Solutions to a Preventable Epidemic* (with Liz Armstrong and Guy Dauncey).

3 Greeniology: How to Live Well, Be Green and Make and Difference. Tanya Ha. Toronto: *Penguin Press*. 2005.

4 Risky Chemicals in the Home and How to Avoid Them (briefing note). *Friends of the Earth UK*. 2004.
(www.foe.co.uk/resource/briefings/risky_chemicals_in_the_home.pdf)

5 Guide to Less Toxic Products (web resource). *Environmental Health Association of Nova Scotia*. (www.lesstoxicguide.ca/print.asp?mode=whole)

6 In-depth: Ingredients, Companies and Safety Gaps. *Environmental Working Group* - Skin Deep Campaign.
(www.ewg.org/reports/skindeep2/findings/index.php?content=phthalates#begin)

Other sources

Safer Shopping Campaign (web resource). *World Wildlife Fund UK*.
(http://safershopping.wwf.org.uk)

Toxic Nation: A Report on Pollution in Canadians. *Environmental Defence*. 2005. (www.environmentaldefense.ca)

Transportation

1 Doctors: Smog Will Kill 5,800 Ontarians This Year (press release). *Ontario Medical Association*. June 14th, 2005.
(www.oma.org/pcomm/pressrel/pr050614.htm)

2 Fuel Consumption Guide, 2005 (guide). *Natural Resources Canada*. 2005. (http://oee.nrcan.gc.ca/publications/transportation/fuel-guide/2005)

3 National Inventory Report: Greenhouse Gas Sources and Sinks in Canada 1990-2005. Published by *Environment Canada*. April 2007.

4. *Greenpeace Canada* energy campaign. Dave Martin, campaigner coordinator. (www.greenpeace.org/canada/en/campaigns/climate-and-energy)

5. Your Guide to the One-Tonne Challenge (guide). Published by the *Government of Canada*. March, 2004.

6. Ibid

7. Clearing the Air: The Myth and Reality of Aviation and Climate Change. Published by the *Climate Action Network Europe* and the *European Federation for Transport and the Environment*. 2006. (www.climnet.org/EUenergy/aviation/2006-06_aviation_clearing_the_air_myths_reality.pdf)

8. This number calculated using a variety of online emissions calculators including *Climate Friendly* (www.climatefriendly.com/flight) and *Atmosfair* (https://www.atmosfair.de/index.php?id=5&L=3)

Other sources

Climate Action Network. www.climateactionnetwork.ca

Consumer's Guide to Effective Environmental Choices - Union of Concerned Scientists. Michael Brower and Warren Leon. New York: *Three Rivers Press*. 1999.

Waste

1. Waste statistics in this section taken from: Human Activity and the Environment: Solid Waste. *The Daily* published by *Statistics Canada*. December 2nd, 2005. (www.statcan.ca/Daily/English/051202/d051202b.htm)

2. The 4 R's - Reduce, Reuse, Recycle, and Recover (web resource). *Environment Canada*. (www.atl.ec.gc.ca/udo/reuse.html)

Water

1. Blue Gold: The Battle Against Corporate Theft of the World's Water. Maude Barlow and Tony Clarke. Toronto: *McClelland & Stewart*. 2002.

2. Ibid

3. Water for Life: Making it Happen. Published by the *World Health Organization* and *Unicef*. 2005. (www.who.int/water_sanitation_health/waterforlife.pdf)

4. Canada foils UN water plan (article). *Toronto Star*. April 2nd, 2008. (http://www.thestar.com/News/Canada/article/409003)

5. Harper government blocks UN resolution on right to water (press release). *Council of Canadians*. March 17th, 2008. (http://www.canadians.org/media/water/2008/17-Mar-08.html)

6. Bottled Water: Pouring Resources Down the Drain (Eco-Economy update). *Earth Policy Institute*. February, 2006. (www.earth-policy.org/Updates/2006/Update51.htm)

7. *Worldwatch Institute*. July, 2003. (www.worldwatch.org/node/1770)

8. Buying a Toilet (fact sheet). *Canada Mortgage and Housing Corporation*. (www.cmhc-schl.gc.ca/en/co/renoho/refash/refash_004.cfm)

END NOTES

9 Toronto's Water Saver Programs (web resource). *City of Toronto.* (www.toronto.ca/watereff/index.htm)

Wood

1 Endangered Ancient Forests (fact sheet). *Greenpeace US.* (www.greenpeace.org/usa/assets/binaries/ancientforests)

2 The World's Last Intact Forest Landscapes (campaign). *Greenpeace International.* (www.intactforests.org)

3 The Amazon's Major Threat: Illegal Logging (press release). *Greenpeace USA.* (Original statistic credited to the *World Resources Institute.*) (www.greenpeace.org/raw/content/usa/press/reports/the-amazon-s-major-threat-ill.pdf)

4 Working With CCA Treated Wood. *Environment Canada.* 2003. (www.ec.gc.ca/EnviroZine/english/issues/20/feature1_e.cfm)

Yard (and garden)

1 Households and the Environment Survey. *The Daily,* published by *Statistics Canada.* November 15th, 2006. (www.statcan.ca/Daily/English/061115/d061115d.htm)

2 Most gardening advice in this section taken from Stepping Lightly on the Earth. Published by *Greenpeace Canada,* circa 1998.

3 Pesticide Reduction (fact sheet). *Sierra Club of Canada.* (www.sierraclub.ca/national/programs/health-environment/pesticides/index.shtml)

Additional general sources

Earth Democracy: Justice, Sustainability and Peace. Vandana Shiva. Cambridge: *South End Press.* 2005.

Feeding the Future. Andrew Heintzman and Evan Solomon (eds.). Toronto: *House of Anansi Press.* 2006.

Fueling the Future. Andrew Heintzman and Evan Solomon (eds.). Toronto: *House of Anansi Press.* 2005.

Genetically Engineered Food: A Self-Defense Guide for Consumers. Ronnie Cummings and Ben Lilliston. New York: *Marlowe & Company.* 2000.

The Green Guide (online magazine). (www.thegreenguide.com)

Greeniology: How to Live Well, Be Green and Make a Difference. Tanya Ha. Toronto: *Penguin Group.* 2005.

Green Living: The E Magazine Guide for Living Lightly on the Earth. New York: *Plume.* 2005.

The No-Nonsense Guide to Climate Change. Dinyar Godrej. Oxford: *New Internationalist Publications Inc.* 2002.

The No-Nonsense Guide to Globalization. Wayne Ellwood. Oxford: *New Internationalist Publications Inc.* 2006.

The Weathermakers. Tim Flannery. Toronto: *HarperCollins.* 2005.

INDEX

INDEX

PHOTOGRAPHY CREDITS

Cover photo: Francis-Lippé Tousignant. Mountain wood sorrel. Canada.

Page 5: Greenpeace. Boreal Forest. Canada.

Page 18: Greenpeace/Daniel Beltra. The Greenpeace ship the Arctic Sunrise makes its way down a river in the Amazon rainforest.

Page 20: Greenpeace/Kate Davison. Thirty Greenpeace activists occupy the Didcot coal-fired power station, the second most polluting power station in Britain.

Page 33: Greenpeace/Michael McCullough. Organic mangoes.

Page 40: Robert J. Brodey.

Page 45: Robert J. Brodey. Clothesline.

Page 46: Greenpeace/Michael McCullough.

Page 52: Greenpeace/Michael McCullough.

Page 55: Greenpeace/Rizman.

Page 56: Greenpeace/Rizman.

Page 59: Greenpeace/Natalie Behring-Chisholm. Electronic equipment—which often contains toxic ingredients—in a scrap yard in Guiyu, China. Electronic equipment is routinely and often illegally shipped as waste, exposing workers and communities to serious health hazards.

Page 60: Greenpeace/Martin Bond.

Page 68: Greenpeace/Kate Davison.

Page 70: Paul Langrock/Zenit/Greenpeace. Offshore wind farm. Denmark.

Page 77: Greenpeace/Daniel Beltra. FSC certified eucalyptus for paper. Chile.

Page 80: Greenpeace/Michael McCullough.

Page 83: Greenpeace/Michael McCullough.

Page 84: Sophia Evans/Greenpeace. Organically grown coffee beans in Comunidade de corrego da Cecilla, Iconha, Brazil.

Page 86: Robert J. Brodey.

Page 88: Greenpeace/Michael McCullough.

Page 89: Greenpeace/Michael McCullough.

Page 91: Greenpeace/Michael McCullough. Reusable Greenpeace mugs.

Page 92: Greenpeace/Michael McCullough.

Page 95: Greenpeace/Michael McCullough. Paint cans.

Page 100: Greenpeace/Michael McCullough.

Page 101: Henry Fair.

Page 102: Robert J. Brodey.

Page 108: Greenpeace/Kate Davison. Toys containing the toxic plastic PVC (1999). London, UK.

Page 112: Greenpeace/Natalie Behring. Dried fish for sale. Pusan, South Korea.

Page 114: Greenpeace/Sari Tolvanen. Blue mussels. Baltic Sea.

Page 115: Greenpeace/Peter Rowlands. Dolphin caught in French driftnet (1991). Azores, North Atlantic.

Page 118: Robert J. Brodey.

Page 120: Greenpeace/Michael McCullough.

Page 121: Robert J. Brodey. Shopping.

Page 122: Greenpeace/Michael McCullough.

Page 124: Greenpeace/Michael McCullough.

Page 128: Robert J. Brodey.

Page 130: Robert J. Brodey.

Page 132: Robert J. Brodey.

Page 138: Greenpeace/Michael McCullough. Public transportation.

Page 142: Greenpeace/Michael McCullough.

Page 142: Greenpeace/Steve Morgan.

Page 144: Greenpeace/Steve Morgan. Garbage dump in Rarotonga, Cook Islands, South Pacific.

Page 146: Greenpeace/Michael McCullough.

Page 150: Greenpeace/Michael McCullough.

Page 153: Greenpeace/Michael McCullough.

Page 158: Greenpeace/Michael McCullough.

Page 160: Greenpeace/Michael McCullough.

Page 177: Clive Shirley/Greenpeace. Forest. Ecuador.

Page 181: David Dodge/ copyright the Pembina Institute. Tailings pond north of Syncrude upgrader, northern Alberta.

Page 187: Greenpeace/Keziere. Lyle Thurston on the original Greenpeace voyage in 1971.

Page 193: Greenpeace/Markus Mauthe. Greenpeace activists are hosed with water cannons while protesting an illegal soy port in the Amazon rainforest (2006).

ACKNOWLEDGEMENTS

Thank you to the incredible campaigners, experts, writers, editors and activists who went through several drafts of this book with endless patience and fine-toothed combs: Josh Brandon, Richard Brooks, Varda Burstyn, Yossi Cadan, Mona Coulavin, Bruce Cox, Eric Darier, Wayne Ellwood from the *New Internationalist Magazine*, Christy Ferguson, Mike Hudema, Brandy Humes, Beth Hunter, Sarah King, Kathy Magher, Dave Martin, Rob Milling, Kai Millyard from Green Communities Canada, Rebecca Moershel, Wanjiru Ndungu, Sharon Oosthoek, Laura Severinac, Shawn-Patrick Stensil, Bev Thorpe, Toni Vernelli and the helpful and knowledgeable Anne Wordsworth. Thank you to Catherine Stewart (Living Oceans Society) for resources. Thank you to the Sage Cafe for letting us photograph their delicious food. Thank you to Grassroots Environmental Products and Strictly Bulk for letting us photograph their eco-conscious merchandise.

Thank you to Rebecca Moershel for spearheading, shaping and realizing this project.

Thank you to Wanjiru Ndungu for her ideas, support and expert coordination.

Thank you to Noël Nanton for his vision, his company and for making this beautiful.

Thank you to Kate Cassidy for her ideas, practical thinking and hawk-eye.

Thank you to Kim Kerridge for her hard work and persistence assembling the endorsements for this book.

Thank you to Michael McCullough and Robert J. Brodey for their beautiful photography.

Thank you to Richard Brooks for his ideas, careful reading and detailed input.

Thank you to John Timmins for helping to shepherd the second edition of this book.

Thank you to Jade Bowen for her incredibly dedicated fact-checking.

Thank you to Joy Woodward for her generous copy-edit.

Thank you to Dawn Promislow for proof-reading.

Thank you to Sheila and Morton Katz.

Thank you to Marlisa Budihardjo,
Mark Cauchi, Wudasie Efrem, Elliot
George, Nuria Gonzalez, Nadia
Molinari, typotherapy and Joerg
Wittenbrinck for input, inspiration
and support.

Thank you also and always to Gila Bell,
Mona Coulavin, Carol Futerman, Anna
Isacsson and Jenny Katz.